The Bumper Compendium of
MIND-BENDING PUZZLES

Lagoon Books, London

Editor: Heather Dickson

Cover, page design and layout: Linley Clode

Published by:

LAGOON BOOKS

PO BOX 311, KT2 5QW, UK

ISBN: 1899712615

© LAGOON BOOKS, 1998

Printed in Singapore.

The Bumper Compendium of

MIND-BENDING
PUZZLES

OTHER TITLES AVAILABLE FROM LAGOON BOOKS:

Mind-Bending Puzzle Books

Mind-Bending Lateral Thinking Puzzles (ISBN 1899712062)

Mind-Bending Lateral Thinking Puzzles – Volume II (ISBN 1899712194)

Mind-Bending Lateral Thinking Puzzles by Des MacHale (ISBN 1899712232)

Mind-Bending Conundrums & Puzzles (ISBN 1899712038)

Mind-Bending Classic Logic Puzzles (ISBN 1899712186)

Mind-Bending Challenging Logic (ISBN 1899712240)

Mind-Bending Classic Word Puzzles (ISBN 1899712054)

Mind-Bending Crossword Puzzles (ISBN 1899712399)

Five-Minute Lateral Thinking Puzzle Books

Five-Minute Classic Lateral Thinking Puzzles (ISBN 1899712291)

Five-Minute Crime Lateral Thinking Puzzles (ISBN 1899712283)

Five-Minute Murder Lateral Thinking Puzzles (ISBN 189971233X)

Five-Minute Adventure Lateral Thinking Puzzles (ISBN 1899712607)

All books can be ordered from bookshops by quoting the above ISBN numbers.

Some titles may not be available in all countries. All titles are available in the UK.

INTRODUCTION

This book offers page after page of some of the world's most popular puzzles and conundrums. Divided into chapters, according to type, you will find some puzzles relatively easy and others more difficult but, remember, all are ultimately possible!

Some of the puzzles selected have been taken from Lagoon's original puzzle books: *Mind-Bending Lateral Thinking Puzzles - Volumes I and II*, *Mind-Bending Classic Logic* and *Mind-Bending Conundrums and Puzzles*. Others have been specially devised for Lagoon by the expert puzzler Des MacHale, who is an Associate Professor of Mathematics at University College Cork, in Ireland, and the author of more than 50 books, including Lagoon's *Mind-Bending Lateral Thinking Puzzles by Des MacHale*.

Continuing the Mind-Bending tradition of cunningly worded puzzles, innovative graphics and stunning presentation, this book has been put together to offer a treat for the eye and a feast for the mind.

INDEX

Puzzles   Chapter

LOGIC
PUZZLES

**A rational mind is an absolute must if
you want to crack these colourful and
inventive classic logic puzzles!**

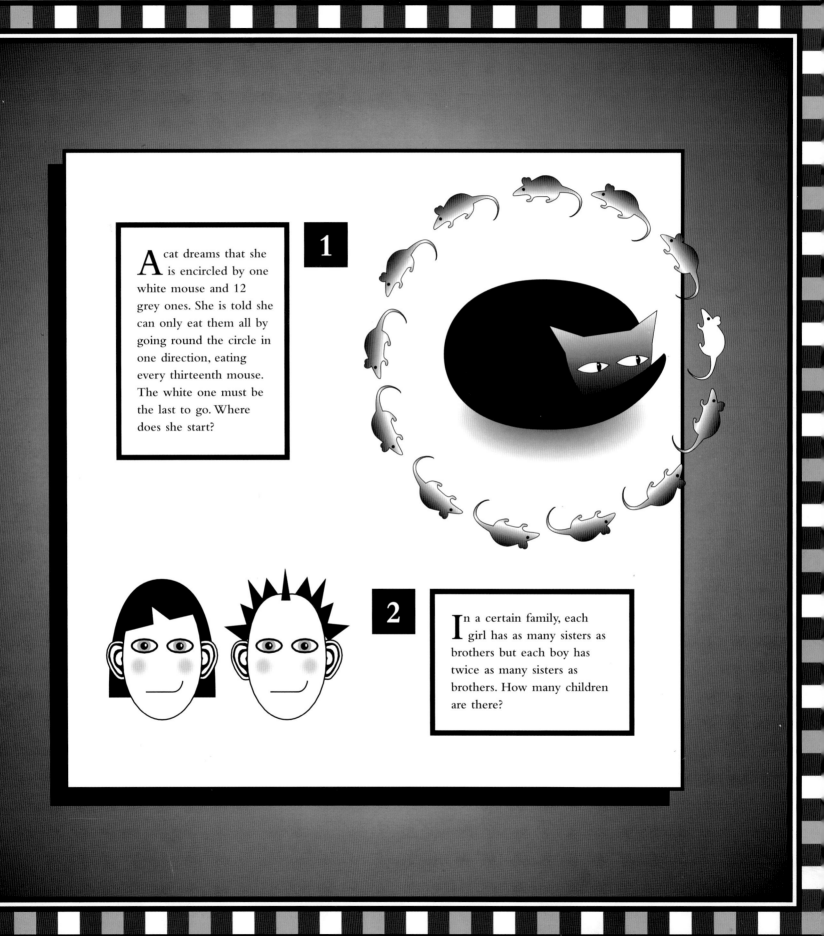

1

A cat dreams that she is encircled by one white mouse and 12 grey ones. She is told she can only eat them all by going round the circle in one direction, eating every thirteenth mouse. The white one must be the last to go. Where does she start?

2

In a certain family, each girl has as many sisters as brothers but each boy has twice as many sisters as brothers. How many children are there?

3

Ma Baker made some pizza dough using extra strong yeast. When left in a warm place it always doubles in size every 24 hours. If it takes 4 days to rise to the top of her extra large bowl, after how long would it be exactly half way up the bowl?

4

Three brothers entered a shop, each needing a pair of shoes re-soled and a key cut. There are two assistants in the shop, both of whom work at the same speed. It takes 15 minutes to re-sole a pair of shoes and 5 minutes to cut a key. How quickly can they finish?

5

A man died leaving all of his money to be divided among his widow, four daughters and three sons. He stipulated that each daughter should receive three times as much as each son, and each son should receive twice as much as their mother. If the exact amount left was £7936, how much should the widow receive?

91

Bill and Ben's combined age is 91. Bill is now twice as old as Ben was when Bill was as old as Ben is now. How old are they?

6

If a pig weighs 30kg plus half its own weight, how much does it weigh?

7

I f four boys can pick four apples in four minutes, how many boys would be able to pick 100 apples in 100 minutes?

8

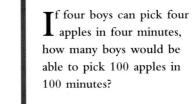

W hen a boat is at anchor, five of the rungs on the rope ladder over its side are underwater. If the rungs are 30cm apart and each one is 3cm thick, how many rungs would be underwater four hours later, if the tide rises at a rate of 35cm per hour?

9

If 8 grapefruit, 7 oranges and 3 lemons weigh the same as 3 oranges, 6 grapefruit and 6 lemons, if a grapefruit weighs 2/3 as much as a lemon and if a dozen oranges weigh 3 kilos...how much does a lemon weigh?

10

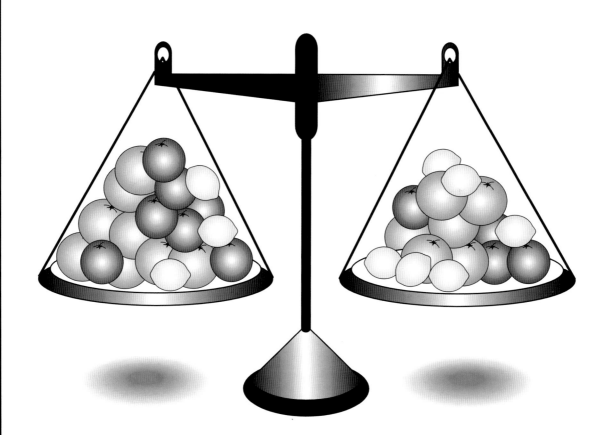

11

If I save 1p on the first day of January, 2p on the second, 4p on the third and continue, each day saving twice as much as the day before, how much will I have saved altogether by the last day of January?

1 2 3...

If six squirrels can eat 6 acorns in 1/10 of an hour, how many would it take to eat 100 acorns in 6000 seconds?

12

13

I have 25 hankies, equally divided into five different colours. If I were blindfolded, how many would I have to pick out to be sure of having one of each colour?

SP

There are two clocks, one of which goes one minute per hour too slow and the other goes thirty seconds per hour too fast. If I wind them up and start them at the same time, how long would it be before one clock was exactly one hour ahead of the other?

14

15

Aunt Tabitha was extremely touchy about her age. When an impudent nephew was brave enough to ask her, she cunningly replied that she was 35 years old, not counting Saturdays or Sundays. So how old was she?

35

16

Sally bought a bracelet for £21 which she then resold for £25. She unwisely accepted a cheque from the purchaser for £35 and gave him £10 change. She then gave the cheque to her landlord but it bounced. She had to borrow a further £35 to pay the rent. How much money has Sally actually lost?

17

If a man spends one-fifth of what is in his wallet and then one-fifth of what remained, and has spent a total of £72.00, what was the amount originally in his wallet?

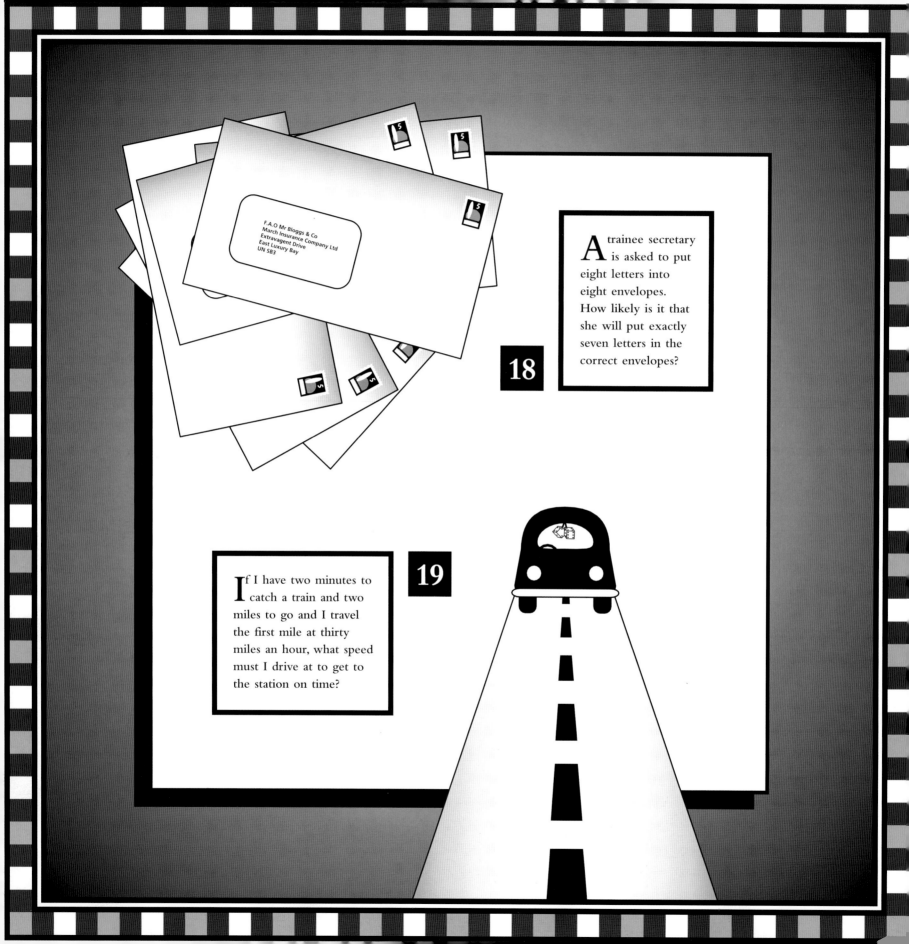

A trainee secretary is asked to put eight letters into eight envelopes. How likely is it that she will put exactly seven letters in the correct envelopes?

18

F.A.O Mr Bloggs & Co
March Insurance Company Ltd
Extravagent Drive
East Luxury Bay
UN 5B3

19

If I have two minutes to catch a train and two miles to go and I travel the first mile at thirty miles an hour, what speed must I drive at to get to the station on time?

Can you cover a 9m by 9m square with 2m by 1m tiles without overlap or leaving any vacant spaces?

20

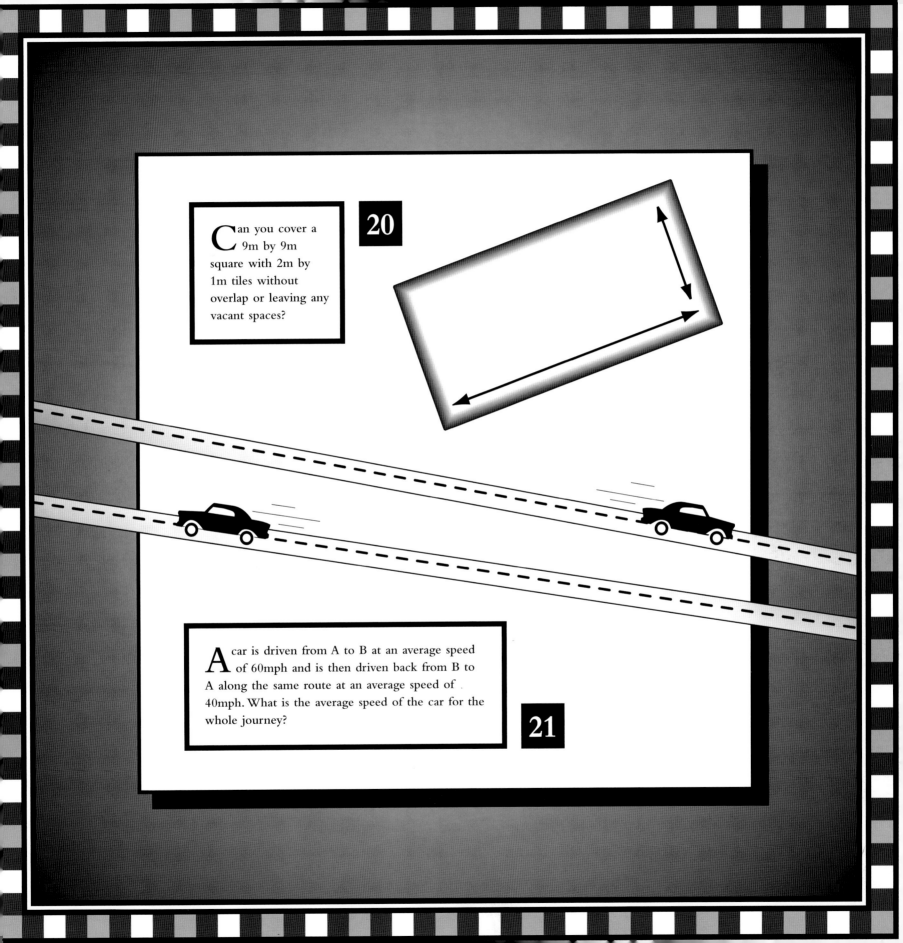

A car is driven from A to B at an average speed of 60mph and is then driven back from B to A along the same route at an average speed of 40mph. What is the average speed of the car for the whole journey?

21

A ferry man has a problem. He has to take a goat, a wolf and a cabbage to the other side of the river. His boat is only big enough to carry two of them at a time. How can he get them safely to the other side without any of them being eaten?

22

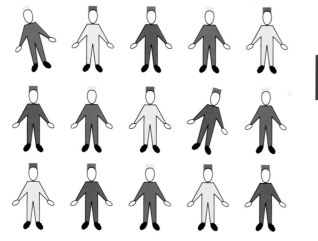

23

Asked about his children, a man replied, "They are all redheads but two, all brunettes but two and all blondes but two". How many children did he have?

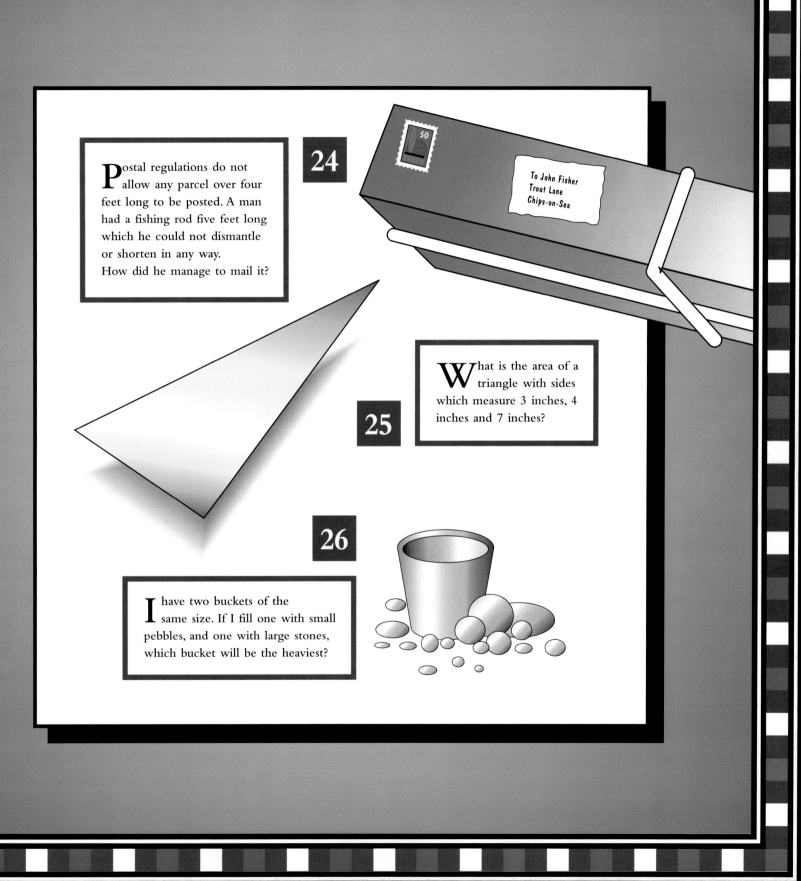

24 Postal regulations do not allow any parcel over four feet long to be posted. A man had a fishing rod five feet long which he could not dismantle or shorten in any way. How did he manage to mail it?

To John Fisher
Trout Lane
Chips-on-Sea

25 What is the area of a triangle with sides which measure 3 inches, 4 inches and 7 inches?

26 I have two buckets of the same size. If I fill one with small pebbles, and one with large stones, which bucket will be the heaviest?

LOGIC PUZZLES - SOLUTIONS

1. If the cat starts at the 5th mouse clockwise or anti-clockwise to the white mouse she will eat the white mouse last

2. Three boys and four girls

3. After 3 days

4. In 30 minutes (one assistant does 1 pair of shoes and 3 keys, the other does 2 pairs of shoes)

5. £256

6. Bill is 52, Ben is 39

7. 60kg

8. Four. As a team, they can - on average - pick one a minute

9. Five. The boat is afloat, so as the tide rises, so does the boat!

10. 600g

11. £21,474,836.47

12. It would take six squirrels to eat 100 acorns in 6000 seconds (100 minutes)

13. 21

14. The faster clock gains on the slow one by the rate of one minute thirty seconds per hour. After 40 hours the faster clock will be exactly one hour ahead

15. 49

16. £31. She has lost the £21 originally spent on the bracelet plus the £10 which she gave as change. She failed to make the £4 profit she hoped for but this cannot count as money lost

17. £200

18. It is impossible - if seven are in the correct envelopes, the eighth would also have to be in the correct envelope

19. It can't be done. It doesn't matter how fast you drive, the available two minutes have been used up driving the first mile

20. No. The maximum number of tiles you could use in the area - without overlap - is 40 tiles, which would leave you with an untiled space measuring 1m by 1m

21. 48mph

22. He should take the goat alone on the first crossing, as there is no danger of the wolf eating the cabbage. He then returns empty and takes the wolf across, but brings the goat back. He then takes the cabbage across, returns empty, and, on his final crossing, takes the goat across for the second time. All three are now on the other side intact

23. 3

24. He placed it diagonally in a box measuring 3 feet by 4 feet

25. Zero - you cannot have a triangle with the sum of its two smaller sides equal to, or less, than the longest side

26. They will both weigh the same - surprisingly, no matter what the size of the stones the proportion of stone to air space remains the same

2

VISUAL PUZZLES

Open your eyes and engage your
brain before you try to solve any of the
questions in this eye-catching chapter of
brain-baffling visual puzzles!

Put the cherry in the glass, moving only two matches.

1

2

What is the smallest number of these discs that have to be moved to make the triangle point downwards?

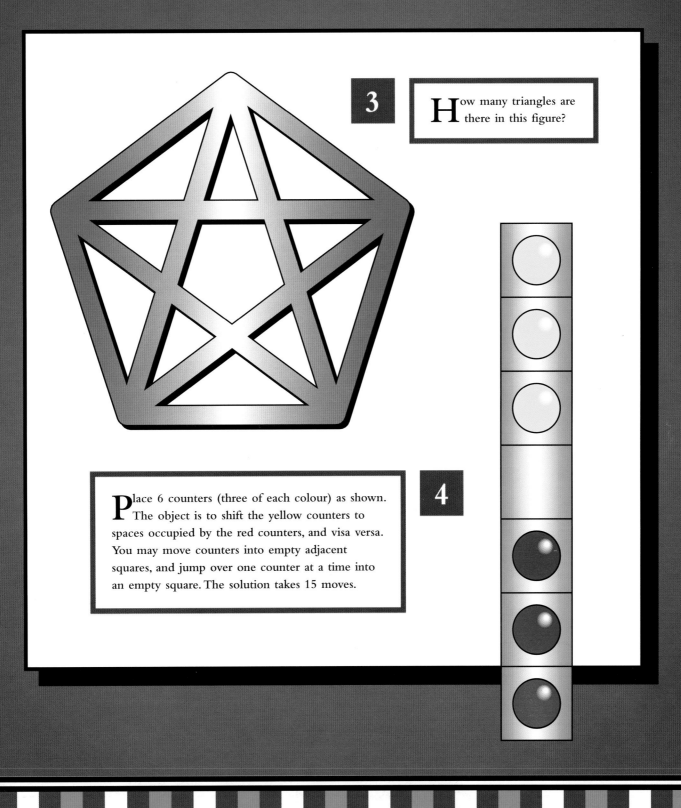

How many triangles are there in this figure?

4

Place 6 counters (three of each colour) as shown. The object is to shift the yellow counters to spaces occupied by the red counters, and visa versa. You may move counters into empty adjacent squares, and jump over one counter at a time into an empty square. The solution takes 15 moves.

Remove six cherries from this square to leave an even number in each line and each column. There are many possible solutions.

5

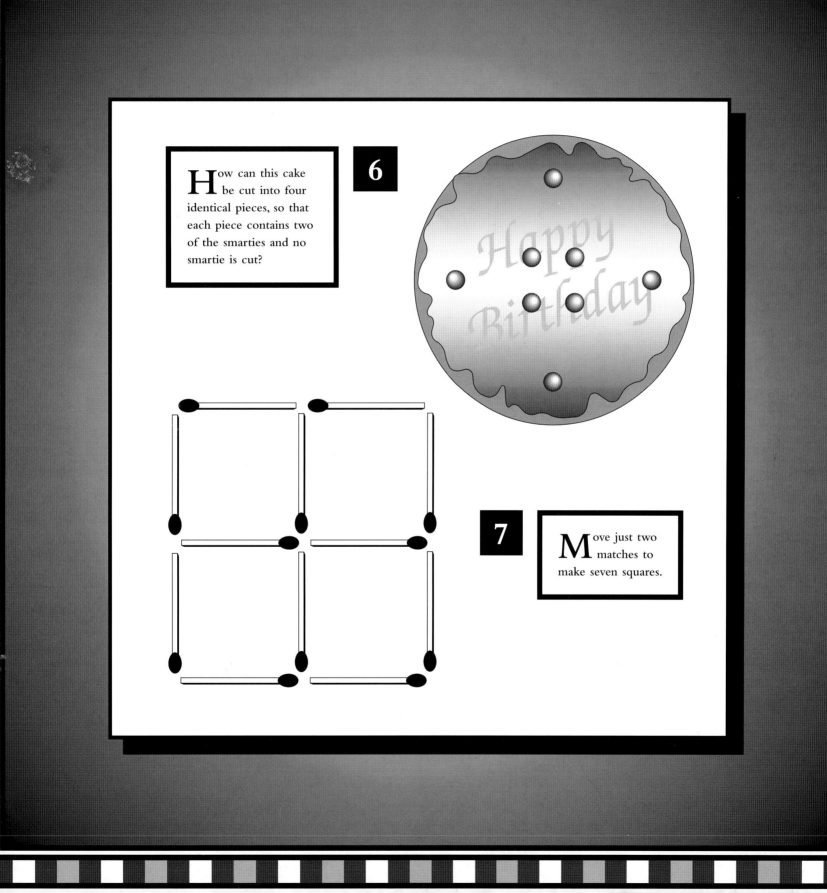

6 How can this cake be cut into four identical pieces, so that each piece contains two of the smarties and no smartie is cut?

Happy Birthday

7 Move just two matches to make seven squares.

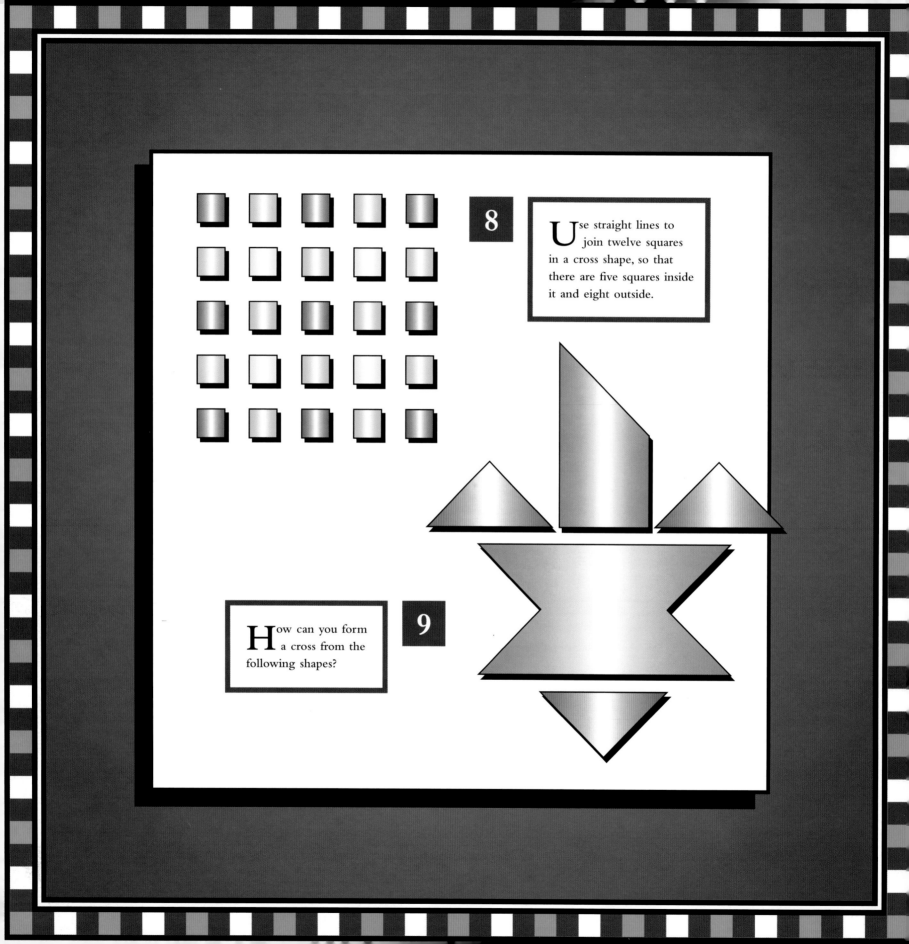

8 Use straight lines to join twelve squares in a cross shape, so that there are five squares inside it and eight outside.

9 How can you form a cross from the following shapes?

Select any one of the star's eight points. Place a counter on that point, and then slide it along a line to the point at the other end. If you repeat this in the correct way, it should be possible to place and slide seven counters, leaving one point vacant.

10

The chain of ribbons shown will only come apart if the middle link is cut. How can three ribbons be linked so that cutting any one of them will free the other two?

11

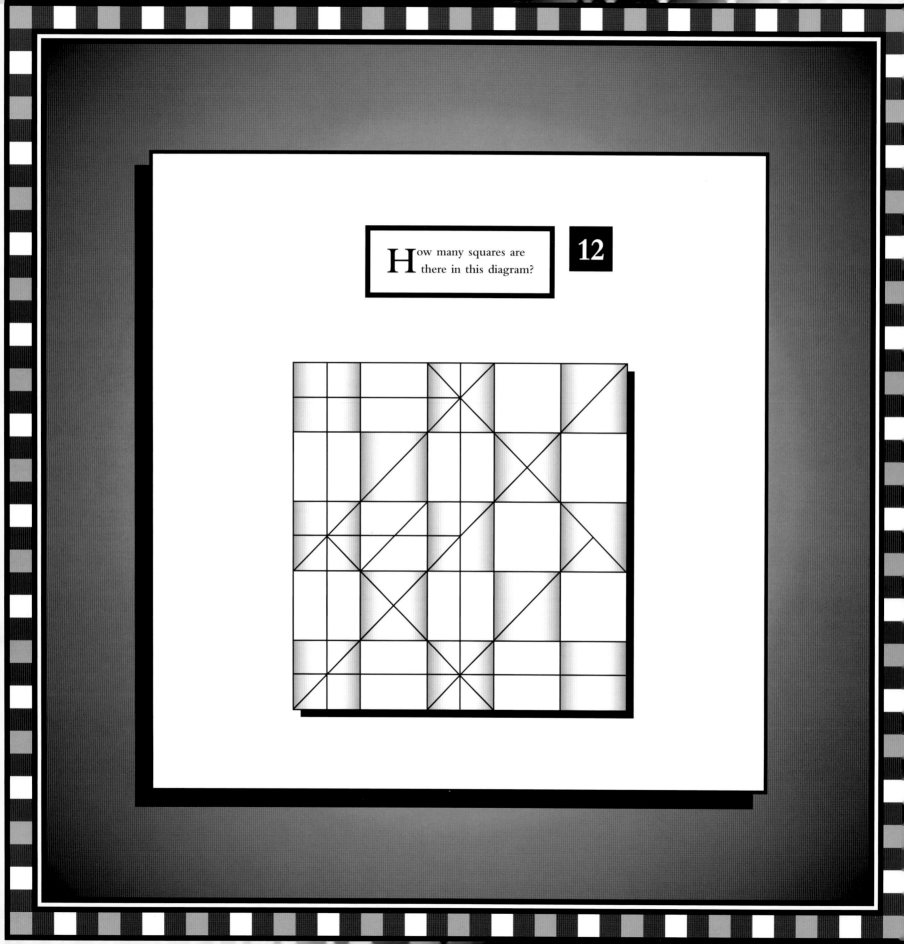

How many squares are there in this diagram?

12

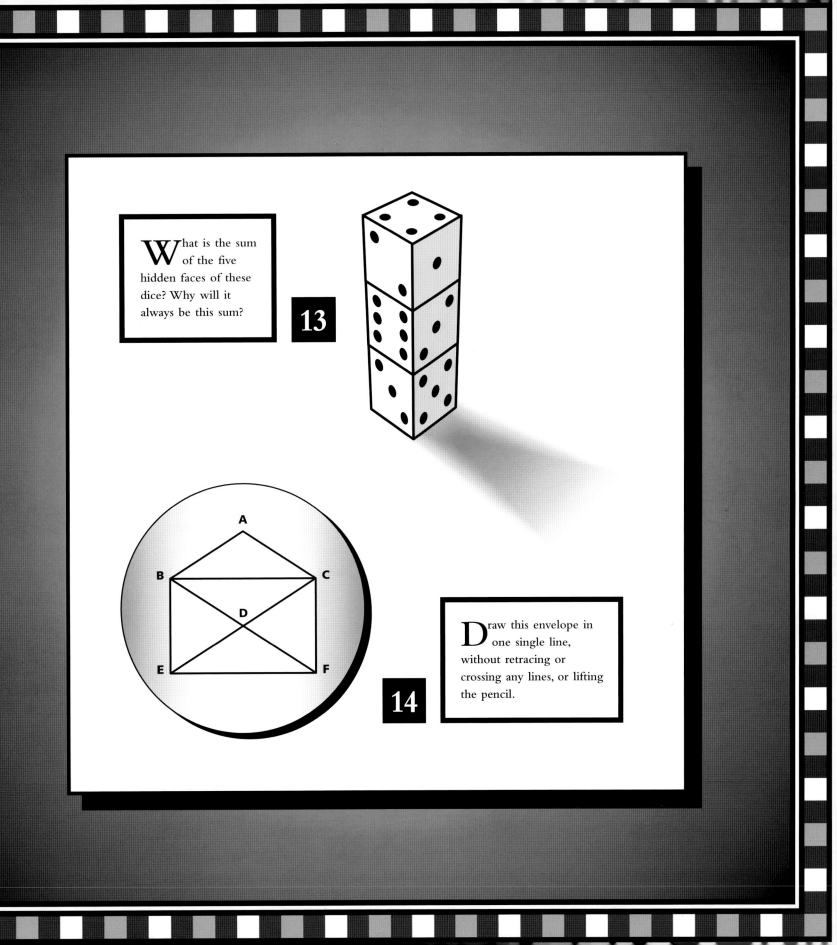

What is the sum of the five hidden faces of these dice? Why will it always be this sum?

13

Draw this envelope in one single line, without retracing or crossing any lines, or lifting the pencil.

14

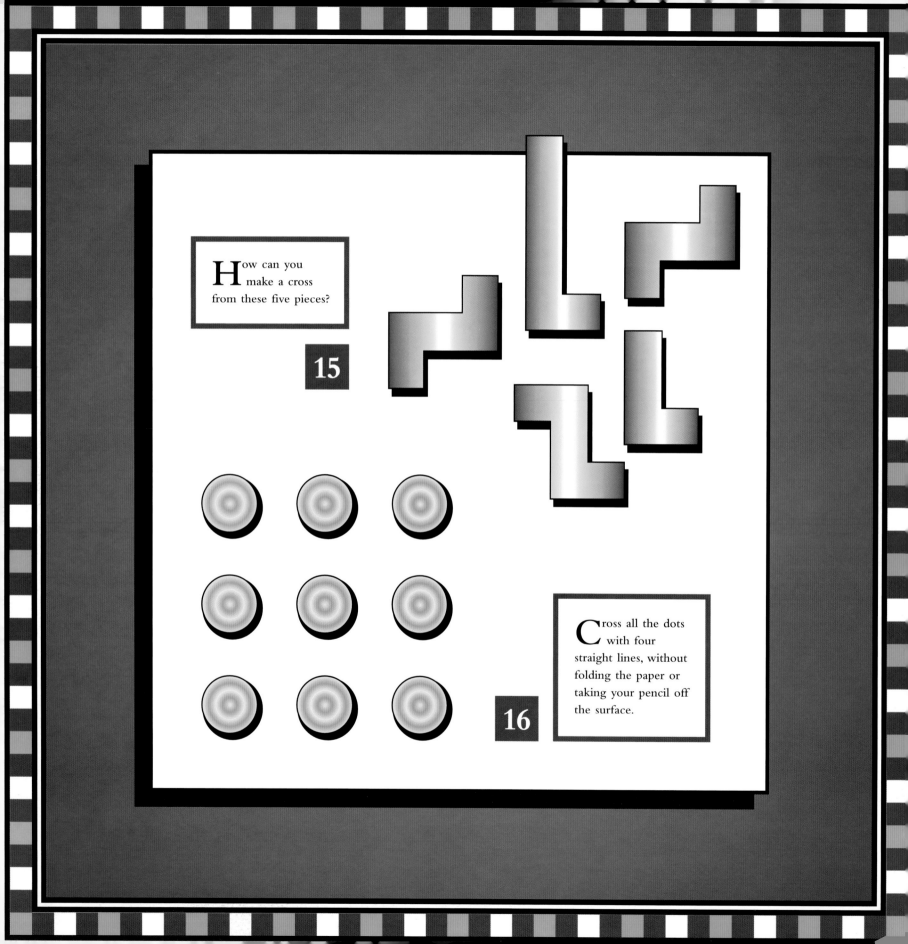

How can you make a cross from these five pieces?

15

Cross all the dots with four straight lines, without folding the paper or taking your pencil off the surface.

16

A general had twenty-eight guards with which to safeguard a princess. He had eight look-out posts and so he arranged his troops as in the diagram, in order to ensure that each wall of the castle was guarded by nine men. At the end of the first day, four men were killed. How could he rearrange the remaining men to ensure that nine men still guard each wall? At the end of the second day a further four men were killed. Can he still ensure that each wall is guarded by nine men?

17

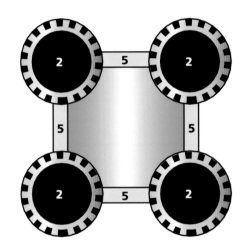

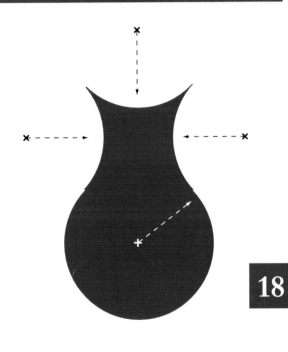

18

How can you cut this jug into 3 parts with 2 straight cuts and form a square from the parts?

There are 145 doors in this prison. Nine of them are locked. The prisoner (represented by the black dot) must find a route to freedom (F). He can go through locked doors by passing through exactly 8 open doors before each one. He doesn't have to go through every open door, but he must go through every cell and all 9 locked doors. He can't go through the same door twice. How does he escape?

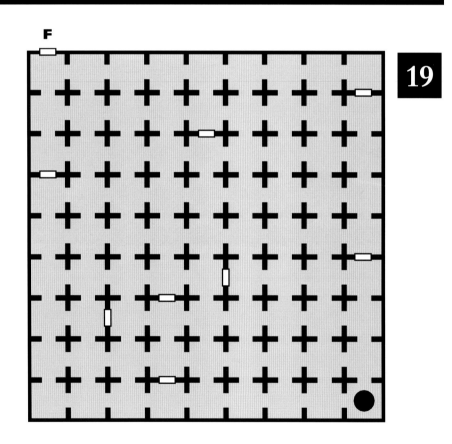

19

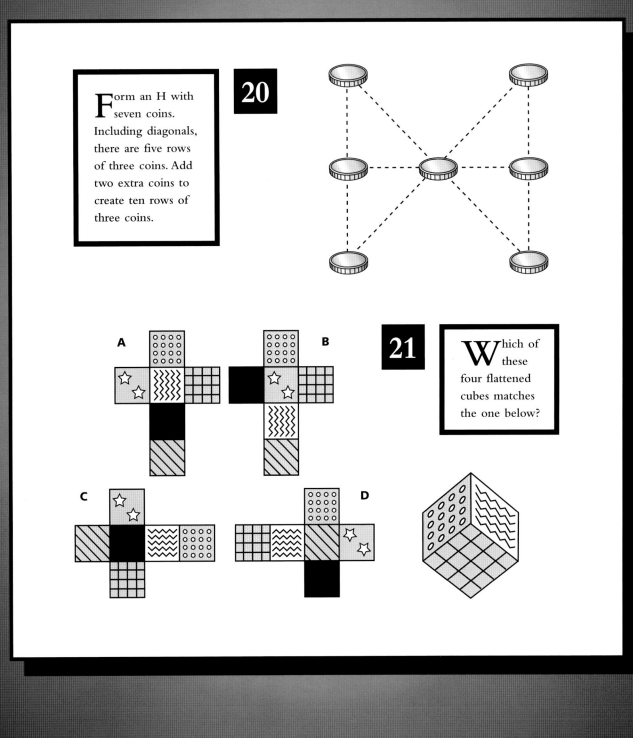

20 Form an H with seven coins. Including diagonals, there are five rows of three coins. Add two extra coins to create ten rows of three coins.

21 Which of these four flattened cubes matches the one below?

A

B

C

D

VISUAL PUZZLES - SOLUTIONS

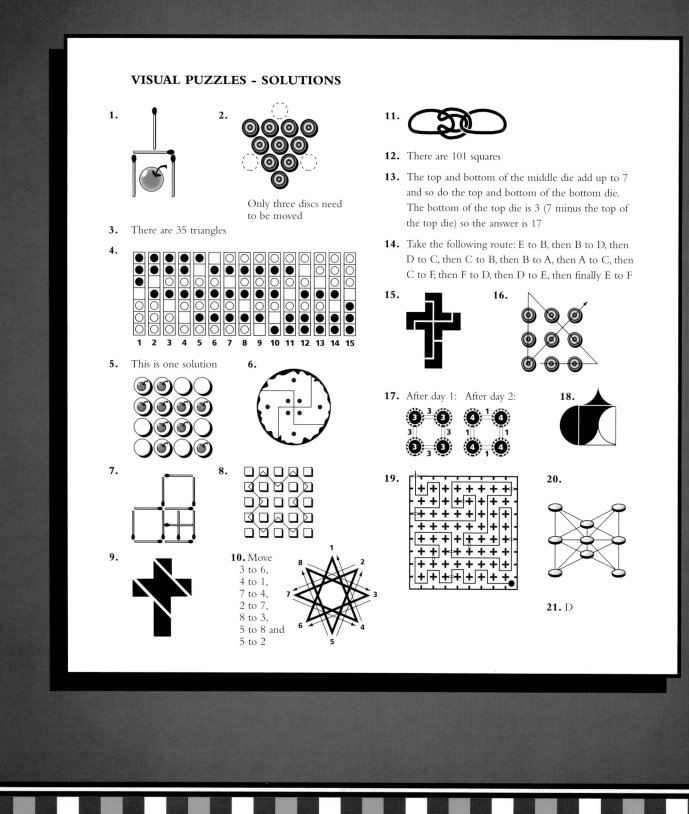

1.

2. Only three discs need to be moved

3. There are 35 triangles

4.

5. This is one solution

6.

7.

8.

9.

10. Move
3 to 6,
4 to 1,
7 to 4,
2 to 7,
8 to 3,
5 to 8 and
5 to 2

11.

12. There are 101 squares

13. The top and bottom of the middle die add up to 7 and so do the top and bottom of the bottom die. The bottom of the top die is 3 (7 minus the top of the top die) so the answer is 17

14. Take the following route: E to B, then B to D, then D to C, then C to B, then B to A, then A to C, then C to F, then F to D, then D to E, then finally E to F

15.

16.

17. After day 1:   After day 2:

18.

19.

20.

21. D

3

LATERAL
THINKING PUZZLES

**You need to be able to throw logic to the wind
and think laterally in order to crack the forty
mind-bending puzzles in this chapter!**

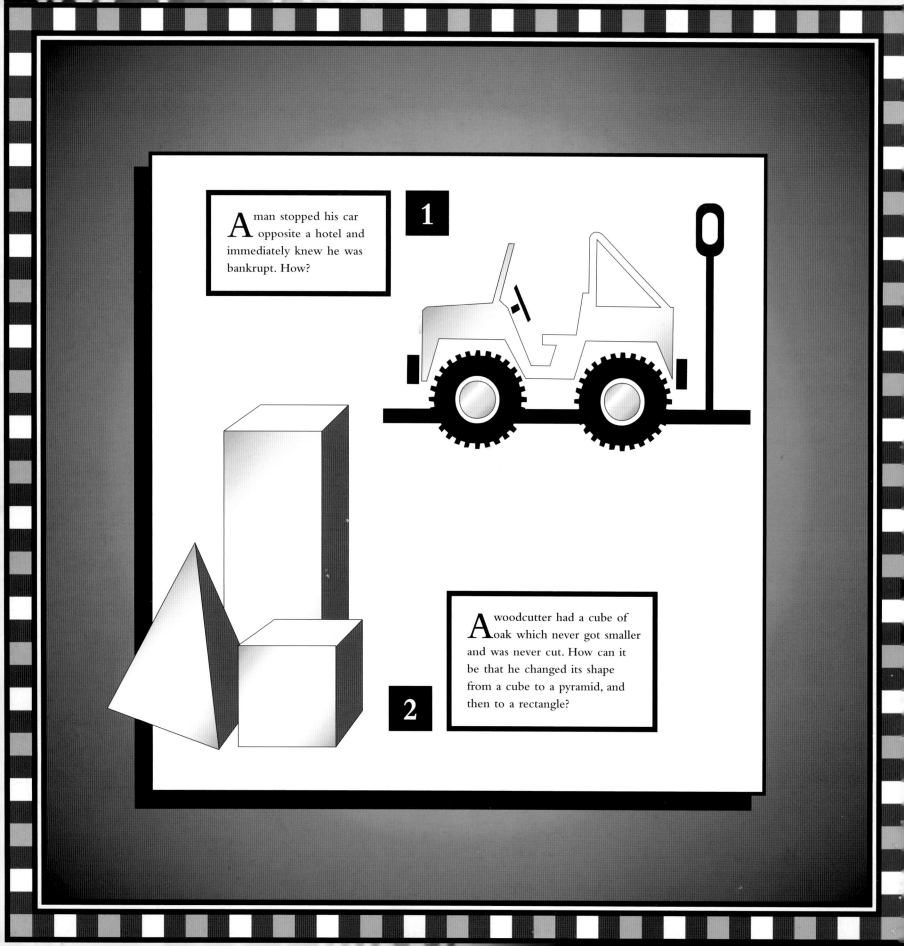

1

A man stopped his car opposite a hotel and immediately knew he was bankrupt. How?

A woodcutter had a cube of oak which never got smaller and was never cut. How can it be that he changed its shape from a cube to a pyramid, and then to a rectangle?

2

3

If a man's mother-in-law can marry his son, and a woman's father can marry her sister-in-law, can a man marry his widow's sister?

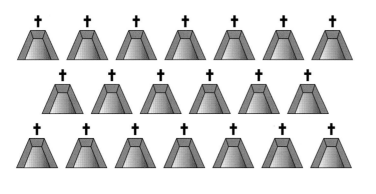

4

An aeroplane carrying sixty Mexican lawyers to a convention in Rio, crashed and landed directly on the border between Columbia, Venezuela and Brazil. Under international law, where should the survivors be buried?

A man looks out of a window. He is desperate to open it, yet he knows this would kill him. Why?

5

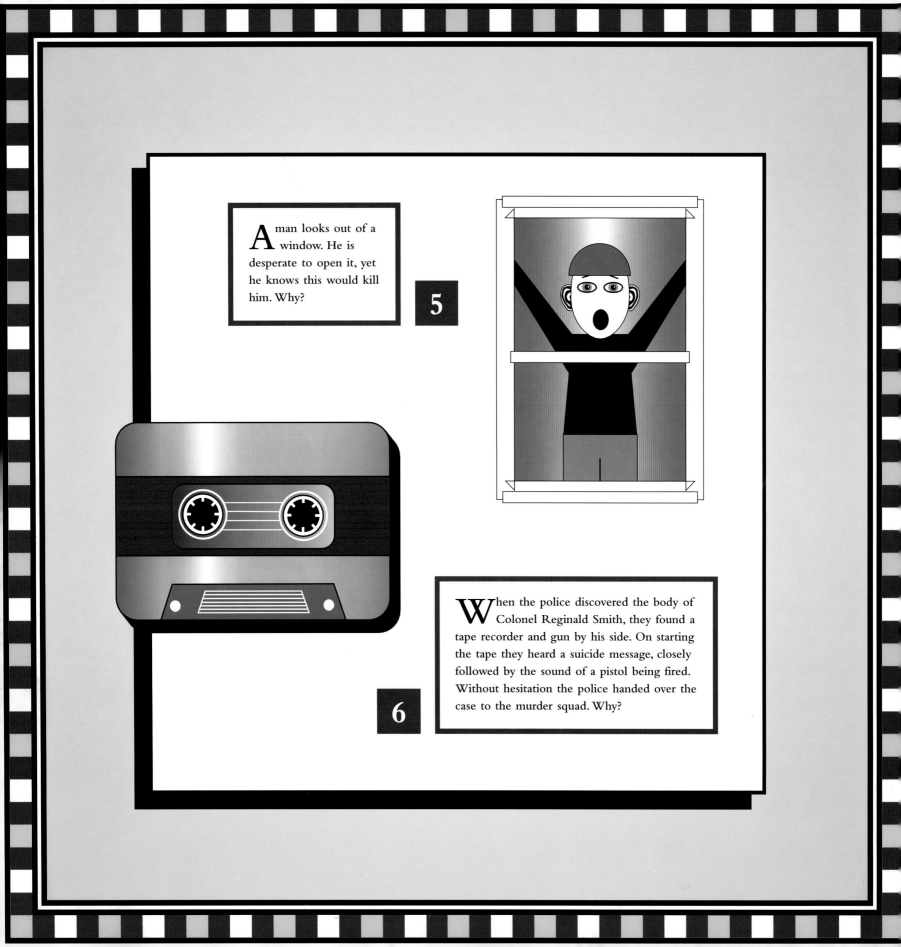

When the police discovered the body of Colonel Reginald Smith, they found a tape recorder and gun by his side. On starting the tape they heard a suicide message, closely followed by the sound of a pistol being fired. Without hesitation the police handed over the case to the murder squad. Why?

6

Tom and Ella emerged from playing in the cellar. Tom had a clean face, but Ella had a dirty smear on her forehead. Why was it Tom who went to wash?

7

A man left a fortune to his two sons. The bulk of the money, however, was to go to the son whose horse finished last in a race between the two. The two sons agonised for days over how they could organise such a race, but eventually they realised it was simple. What could they do?

8

Polly Warden loved the colour yellow. All the walls in her new bungalow were primrose yellow. The carpets, curtains and all the soft furnishings were a golden yellow. What colour were her stairs?

9

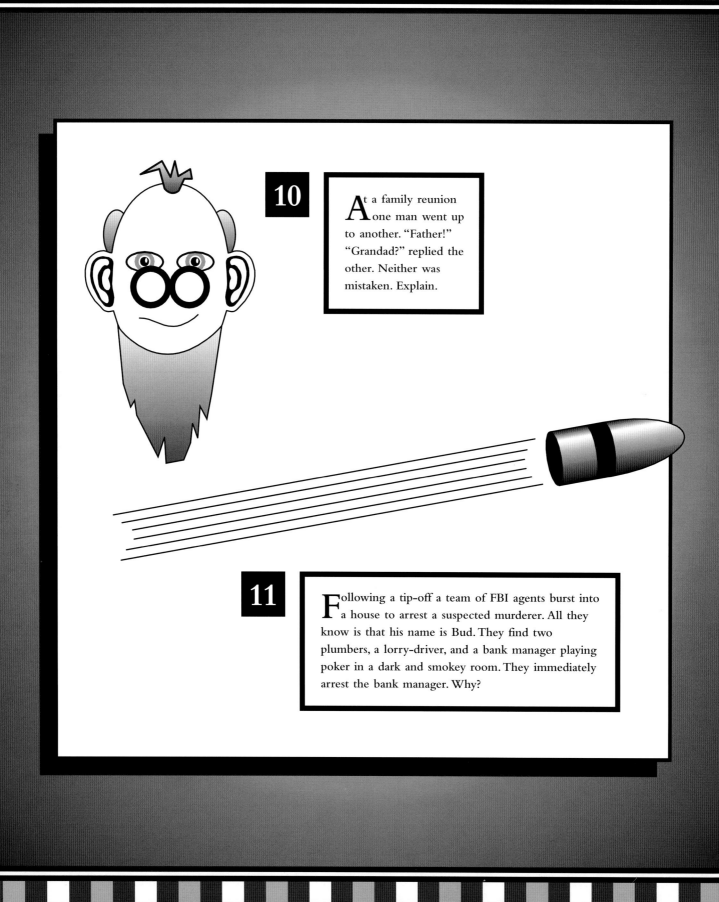

10

At a family reunion one man went up to another. "Father!" "Grandad?" replied the other. Neither was mistaken. Explain.

11

Following a tip-off a team of FBI agents burst into a house to arrest a suspected murderer. All they know is that his name is Bud. They find two plumbers, a lorry-driver, and a bank manager playing poker in a dark and smokey room. They immediately arrest the bank manager. Why?

12

If I walked without an umbrella or a raincoat or a hat across a treeless plain for an hour, how did I avoid getting wet?

9lbs

9lbs

13

A woman was being chased through the jungle by a tribe of hunters. She had in her possession two solid gold ingots which weighed 9lb each. She came to a rope bridge which she needed to cross, but which she knew could only support 125lb in weight. She herself weighed 110lb. She did not have time to carry the ingots across one at a time and it was too far to throw them. She did not have any shoes which she could remove, and the hunters were getting closer with every second. How did she escape with both gold ingots?

A princess is kidnapped by her cruel uncle, who has planned for her to marry one of his two sons. He gave her an ultimatum - she was to make a solitary statement. If what she said was true, she was to marry her elder cousin Johans the Vain, however, if what she said was false, she was to marry the younger son Derek the Dismal. What did she say which allowed her to remain a single girl?

14

15

I often go to the police station, sometimes in the middle of the night, and destroy considerable numbers of fingerprints. I do not, however, consider myself a criminal. Who am I?

16

A prisoner was made to carry a heavy sandbag from one side of the compound to the other. When he got to the other side, he had to take it back again. This went on, hour after hour, day after day, until the prisoner realised that he could put something in the bag that would make it lighter. What was it?

17

I have only a 25, a 10 and three 5 cents coins, yet I can still make 30 cents with two coins even though one of them is not the 25 cents coin. How?

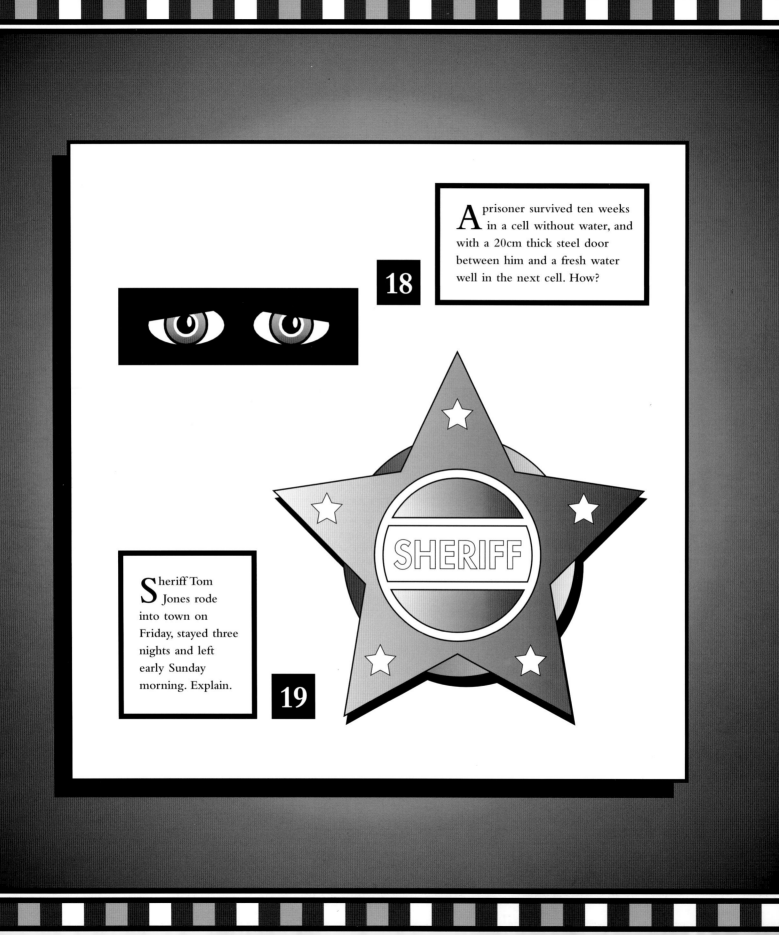

18

A prisoner survived ten weeks in a cell without water, and with a 20cm thick steel door between him and a fresh water well in the next cell. How?

19

Sheriff Tom Jones rode into town on Friday, stayed three nights and left early Sunday morning. Explain.

SHERIFF

20

Racing driver Ramon Ricard had a terrible accident at Daytona leaving him in hospital for 6 months. Surprisingly, he never once considered giving up racing. Why not?

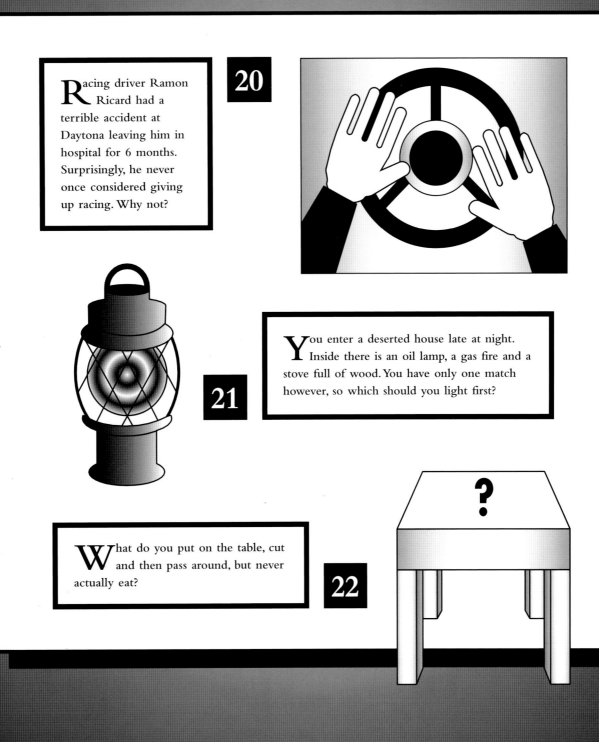

21

You enter a deserted house late at night. Inside there is an oil lamp, a gas fire and a stove full of wood. You have only one match however, so which should you light first?

What do you put on the table, cut and then pass around, but never actually eat?

22

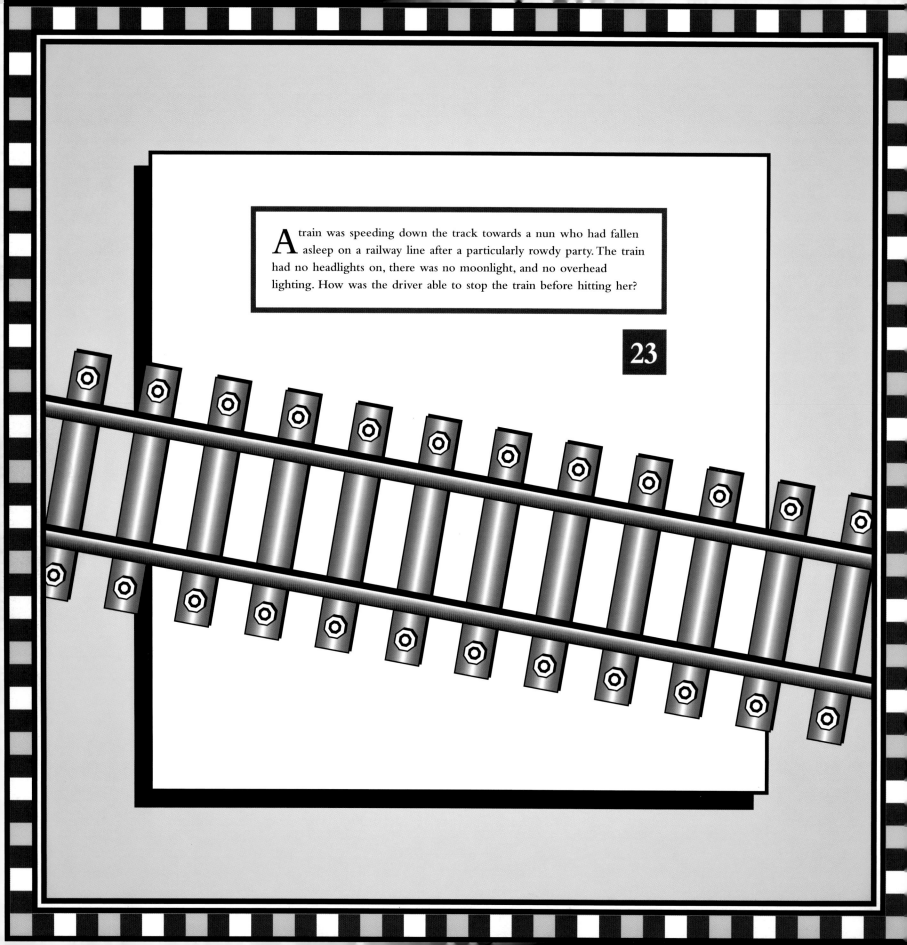

A train was speeding down the track towards a nun who had fallen asleep on a railway line after a particularly rowdy party. The train had no headlights on, there was no moonlight, and no overhead lighting. How was the driver able to stop the train before hitting her?

23

Two miners were sitting on a bench. One miner was the other one's son, but the other one was not his father. Why?

24

1984

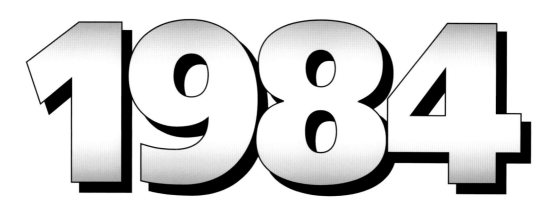

25 Why are 1984 bottles of whisky more valuable than 1977 bottles of whisky?

26

I bumped into my long-lost uncle from Alaska in the street. I'd never met him, seen his picture or heard him described, yet I recognised him immediately. How?

27

A stranger entered a bar and ordered a glass of water. The barmaid said nothing, but grabbed a gun and aimed it at his head. Why did the man simply smile, thank her, and then leave?

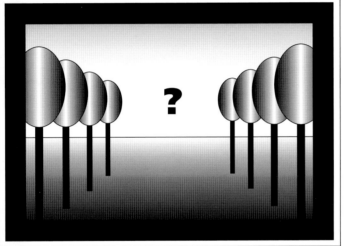

28

At 8:34 precisely, on the day that President Nixon resigned, he looked out of a south facing White House window but couldn't see the top of the Empire State Building. Why not?

29

If an average hen's egg is 5cm long and weighs 300 grams, and an average peacock's egg is exactly twice the length and 2.5 times the weight, which has the greater circumference?

Two fathers and two sons enter a shop and spend £1.50 each. The shopkeeper takes £4.50. What happened to the rest?

30

What occurs once in June, once in July, but twice in August?

31

1	2	3	4	5	6	7
8	9	10	11	12	13	14
15	16	17	18	19	20	21
22	23	24	25	26	27	28
29	30	31				

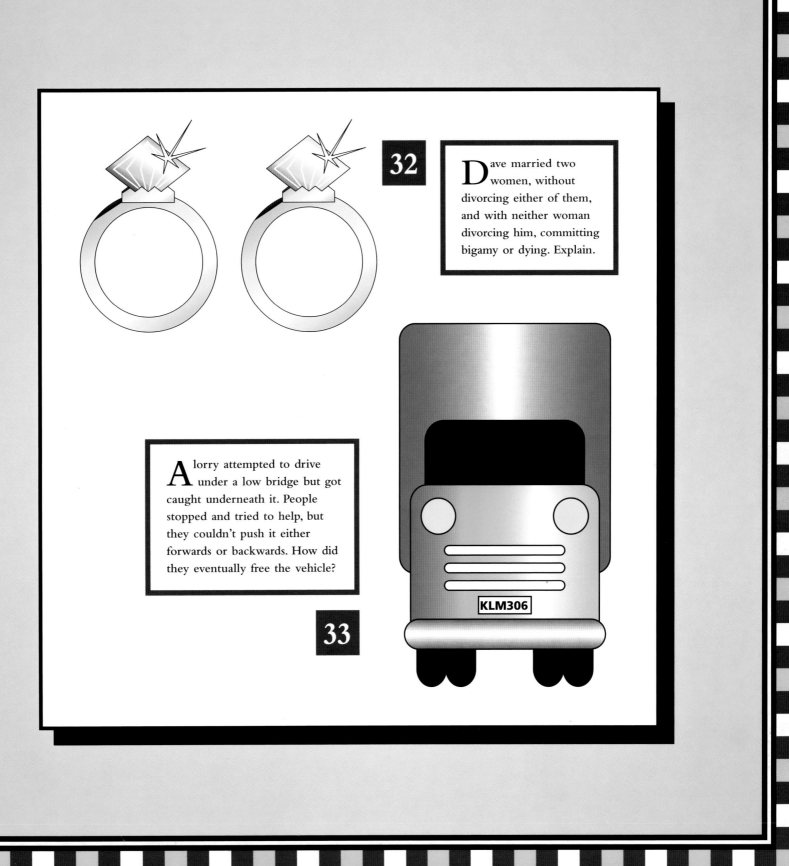

32

Dave married two women, without divorcing either of them, and with neither woman divorcing him, committing bigamy or dying. Explain.

A lorry attempted to drive under a low bridge but got caught underneath it. People stopped and tried to help, but they couldn't push it either forwards or backwards. How did they eventually free the vehicle?

33

KLM306

Two Scrabble champions played five games of Scrabble. Each won and lost the same number of games and there were no draws. How is this possible?

34

35

A man walked into a bar, put £1 on the table and asked for half a pint of lager. The barmaid asked whether he would like Kronenburg or Fosters. He asked for Kronenburg. A little later, another man entered the bar, put £1 on the table and asked for half a pint of lager. She immediately pulled him half a pint of Kronenburg. Why?

A man runs to the quayside, performs a death-defying leap and lands safely but painfully on the deck of a ferry. He is very happy, until an impressed stranger asks him a question, whereupon he starts crying. What is the question?

36

37

Detective Smith finds Romeo and Juliet dead on the kitchen floor surrounded by broken glass. They were alone when they died. What killed them?

The guard of an open prison was given strict instructions not to allow any prisoner to leave the prison without release papers, or to allow any visitor into the prison without written permission from the governor. The guard watched over a strip of land which was the only way into or out of the prison. He knew it would take at least 9 – 10 minutes for anyone to cross the land, and so checked it every five minutes. How did a prisoner make a successful escape, despite having no release papers?

38

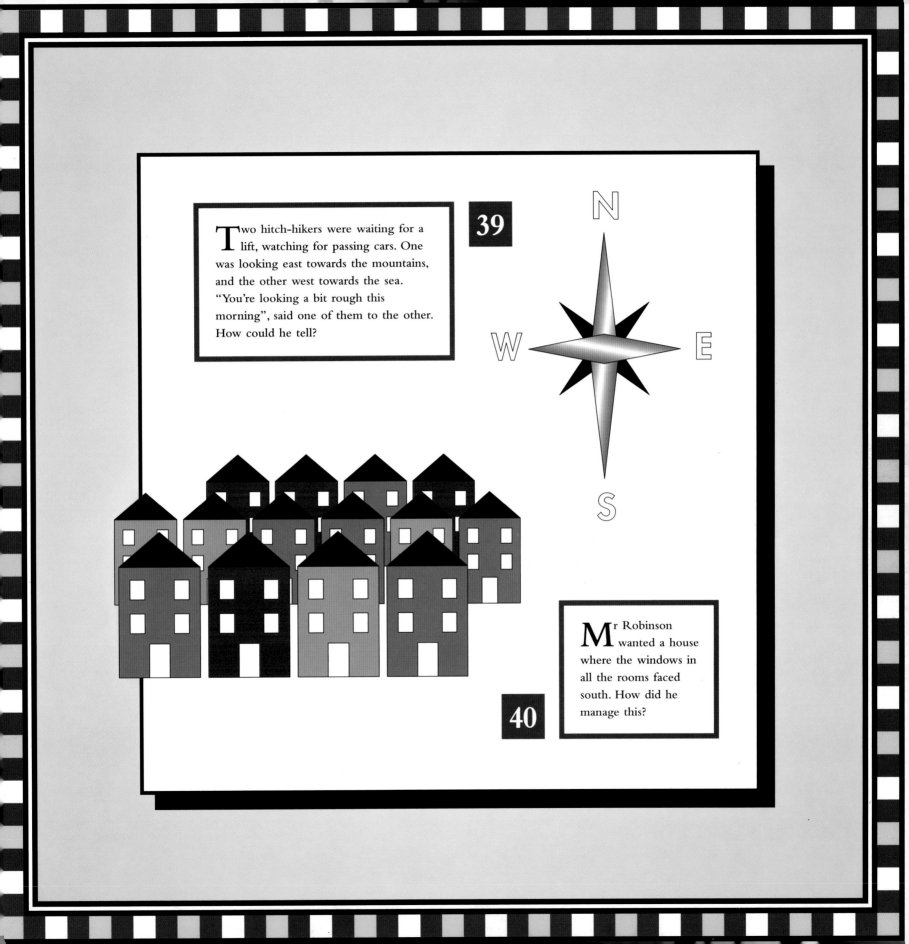

39

Two hitch-hikers were waiting for a lift, watching for passing cars. One was looking east towards the mountains, and the other west towards the sea. "You're looking a bit rough this morning", said one of them to the other. How could he tell?

N
W   E
S

40

Mr Robinson wanted a house where the windows in all the rooms faced south. How did he manage this?

LATERAL THINKING PUZZLES - SOLUTIONS

1. He was playing Monopoly

2. The wood was sawdust which he poured into appropriately shaped containers

3. No, because he would have to be dead in order to have a widow

4. You do not bury survivors

5. He is in a submarine suffering from claustrophobia

6. Because the tape was already rewound, ready for them to listen to

7. They looked at each other! The clean child saw the other's dirty face and assumed that he was as dirty. The child who was dirty only saw the other's clean face so had no reason to think that she was not also clean herself

8. Swap horses and race against each other

9. There are no stairs in a bungalow

10. The grandson was a priest

11. The plumbers and lorry-driver were women, so only the bank manager could be "Bud"

12. It wasn't raining

13. She walked across, juggling the ingots

14. She said: "I will marry Derek the Dismal." If her uncle did marry her to Derek then her statement will have been true, so he should have married her to Johans instead. But if he did marry her to Johans, then her statement would have been false. The uncle had no alternative but to let her go

15. The police station cleaner

16. A hole

17. By using a 25 and a 5 cents coin. Although one of them is not the 25 cents, the other one is

18. The door wasn't locked

19. Friday is the name of his horse

20. Because he fell down the stairs

21. The match

22. A deck of cards

23. It was midday so the driver saw her

24. She was his mother

25. Because there are seven more of them. It is easy to assume that the numbers are dates rather than quantities

26. He is my dad's identical twin

27. The stranger was suffering from hiccups, which is why he asked for some water. The barmaid realised this and drew the gun in order to give the man a shock. This worked, the man was cured of his hiccups and, no longer needing the water, left

28. Because the White House is in Washington and the Empire State in New York

29. Peacocks do not lay eggs

30. Only three men entered the shop, a son, father and grandfather, so only £4.50 was spent

31. The letter U

32. Dave is a priest who conducted two weddings

33. They let some air out of the tyres thus allowing them to push the vehicle free

34. They were not playing each other

35. The tariff displays two different prices, Kronenburg is £1 per half and Fosters is 90p. The first man put a one pound coin on the table (so may have required some change depending on his choice of lager), the second put down a fifty pence piece, two twenties and a ten

36. "Why didn't you wait another two minutes for the ferry to dock?" The ship was coming in, not leaving (as the man had presumed)

37. Romeo and Juliet were goldfish whose bowl was knocked over by an intruding dog. They died from asphyxiation

38. When the guard was in his hut the prisoner began to walk away from the prison. He walked for nearly five minutes and then turned around and started to walk back towards the prison. When he reached the guard, he did not have any permission paper to enter, and so the guard sent him back - to his freedom!

39. They were facing each other

40. He built a house on the North pole so all four sides faced south

4

MAGIC SQUARES AND CIRCLES

Eight enchanting number grids to test and tease the old grey matter!

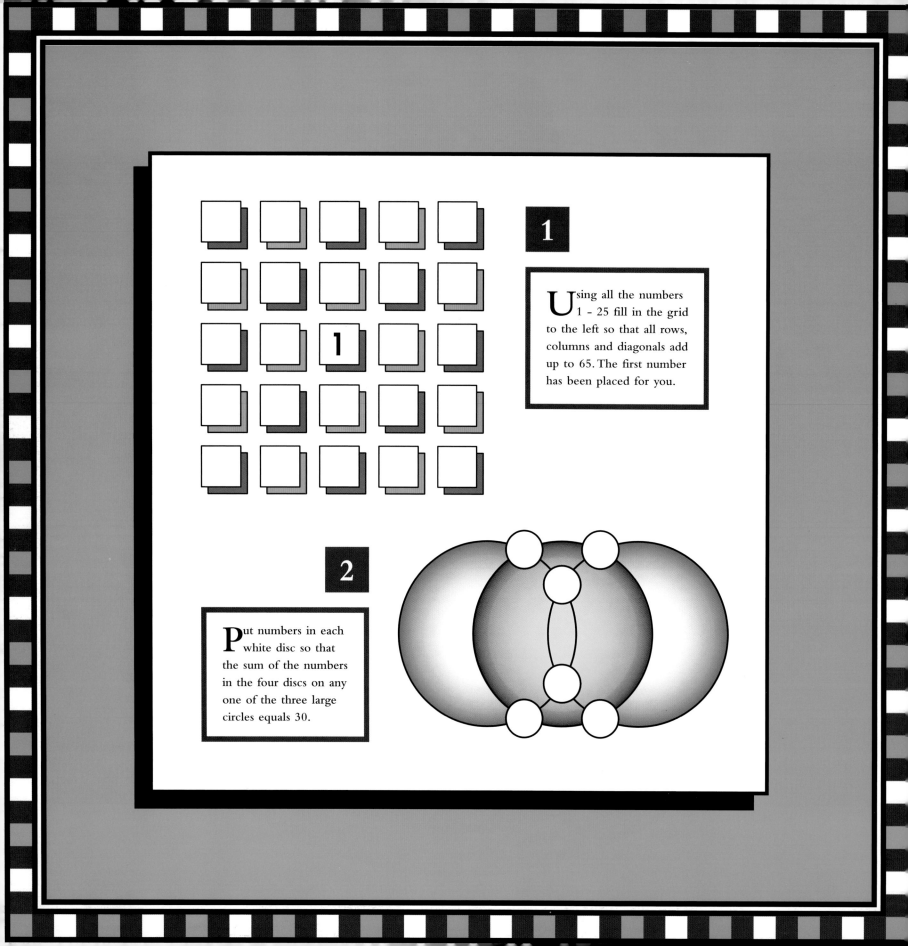

1

Using all the numbers 1 - 25 fill in the grid to the left so that all rows, columns and diagonals add up to 65. The first number has been placed for you.

2

Put numbers in each white disc so that the sum of the numbers in the four discs on any one of the three large circles equals 30.

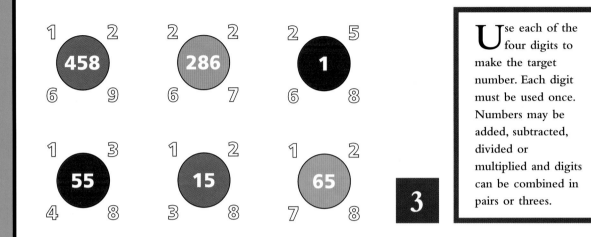

1 458 2
6   9

2 286 2
6   7

2 1 5
6   8

1 55 3
4   8

1 15 2
3   8

1 65 2
7   8

3

U se each of the four digits to make the target number. Each digit must be used once. Numbers may be added, subtracted, divided or multiplied and digits can be combined in pairs or threes.

4

A rrange the numbers 1 to 9 in the cells of this square so that the horizontals, verticals and diagonals all add up to the same number.

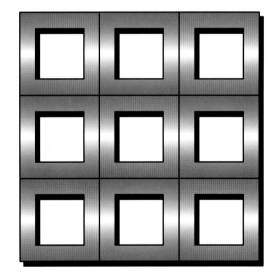

Use the numbers 0 - 15 to fill in the diagram so that the numbers in each circle and on each straight line of four add up to 30.

5

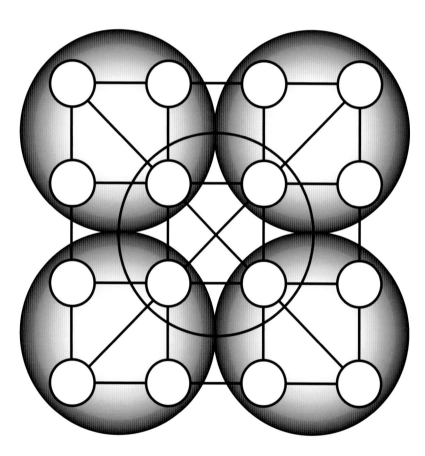

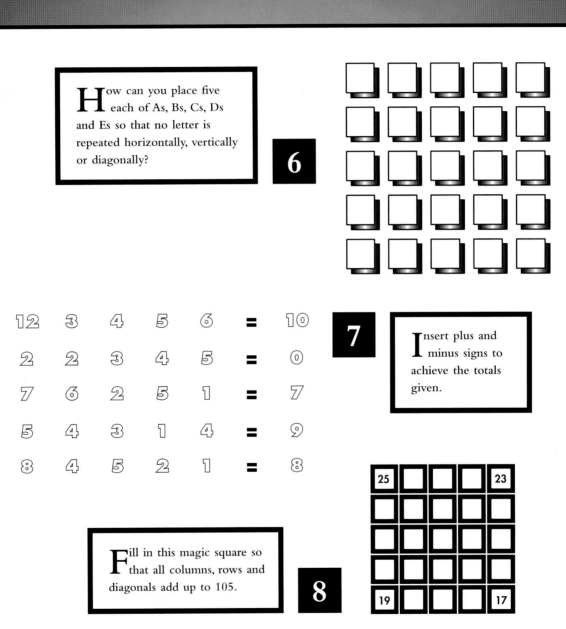

How can you place five each of As, Bs, Cs, Ds and Es so that no letter is repeated horizontally, vertically or diagonally?

6

12	3	4	5	6	=	10
2	2	3	4	5	=	0
7	6	2	5	1	=	7
5	4	3	1	4	=	9
8	4	5	2	1	=	8

7 **I**nsert plus and minus signs to achieve the totals given.

Fill in this magic square so that all columns, rows and diagonals add up to 105.

8

25				23
19				17

MAGIC SQUARES AND CIRCLES – SOLUTIONS

1.

9	11	18	5	22
3	25	7	14	16
12	19	1	23	10
21	8	15	17	4
20	2	24	6	13

2.

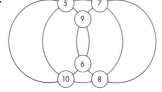

3. Some possibilities are:

$916 \div 2 = 458$

$(7 + 6) \times 22 = 286$

$(5 - 2) - (8 - 6) = 1$

$(4 + 3) \times 8 - 1 = 55$

$31 - (2 \times 8) = 15$

$71 - (8 - 2) = 65$

4.

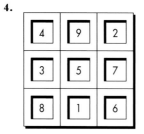

5.

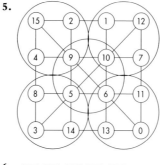

6.

A	B	C	D	E
C	D	E	A	B
E	A	B	C	D
B	C	D	E	A
D	E	A	B	C

7.

$12 + 3 - 4 + 5 - 6 = 10$

$2 + 2 - 3 + 4 - 5 = 0$

$7 - 6 + 2 + 5 - 1 = 7$

$5 + 4 - 3 - 1 + 4 = 9$

$8 - 4 + 5 - 2 + 1 = 8$

8.

25	32	9	16	23
31	13	15	22	24
12	14	21	28	30
18	20	27	29	11
19	26	33	10	17

The above are just some of many possible solutions

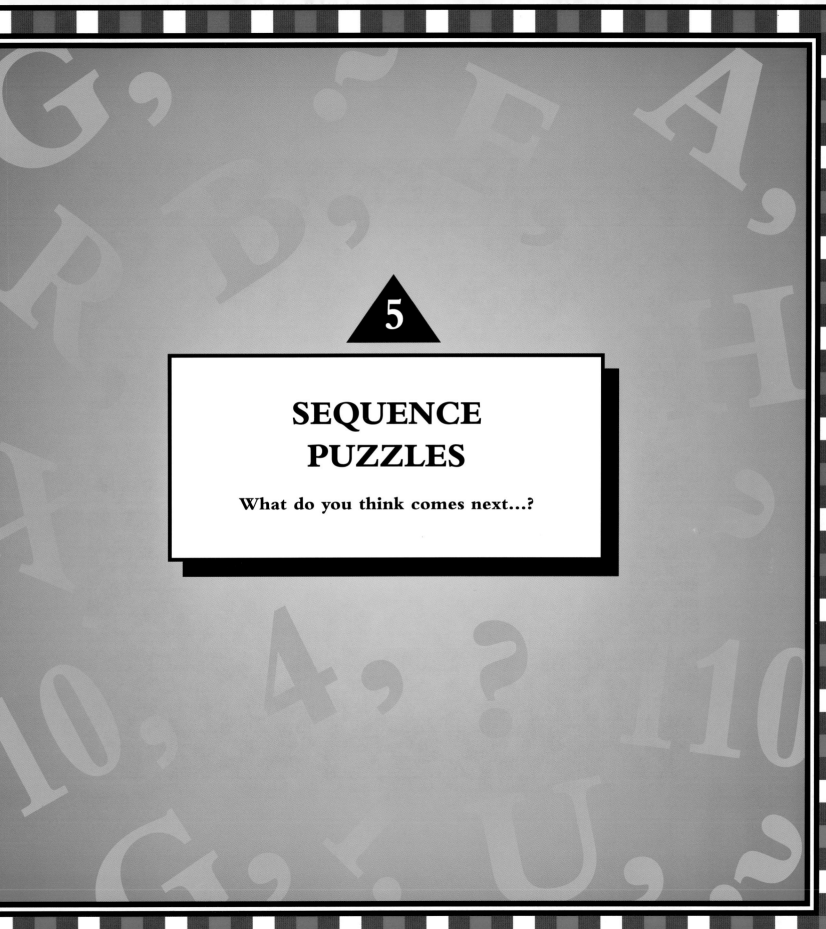

5

SEQUENCE PUZZLES

What do you think comes next...?

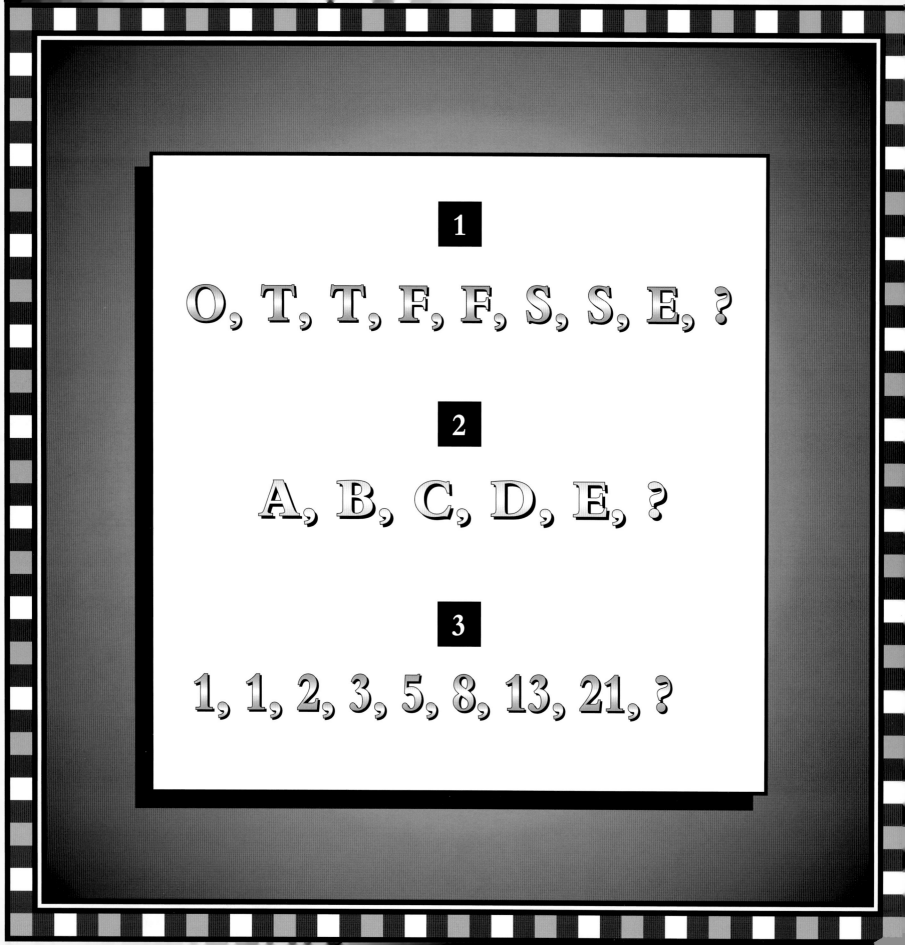

1

O, T, T, F, F, S, S, E, ?

2

A, B, C, D, E, ?

3

1, 1, 2, 3, 5, 8, 13, 21, ?

4

D, N, O, S, A, J, J, M, ?

5

2, 3, 5, 7, 11, 13, 17, 19, 23, ?

6

S, M, H, D, W, M, ?

7

C, D, I, L, M, V, ?

8

T, Q, P, H, H, O, N, ?

9

3, 3, 5, 4, 4, 3, 5, 5, ?

10

K, Q, R, B, K, ?

11

B, C, D, F, G, H, ?

12

1, 3, 6, 10, 15, 21, ?

13

B, C, D, E, H, I, K, O, ?

14

8, 5, 4, 9, 1, ?

15

H, C, D, ?

16

E, O, E, R, E, X, N, T, E, ?

17

F, 4, E, S, 9, S, E, 5, E, ?

18

A, P, A, T, G, C, L, V, L, S, ?

19

1884, 1888, 1892, 1896, ?

20

A, K, Q, J, T, N, E, ?

21

G, E, L, N, D, J, J, ?

22

1, 10, 11, 100, 101, 110, 111, ?

23

A, A, A, A, C, C, C, D, F, G, H, I, I, I, ?

24

A, E, A, P, A, U, U, U, E, C, O, ?

25

202, 122, 232, 425, 262, 728, ?

SEQUENCE PUZZLES - SOLUTIONS

1. N for Nine; these are the initial letters of the numbers one, two, three...

2. K; the vitamins

3. 34; each number is the sum of the previous two numbers. 8 + 13 = 21, 13 + 21 = 34

4. A for April; these are the initial letters of the months of the year, backwards

5. 29; the prime numbers ie numbers that have no factors except one and themselves

6. Y for Year; the various divisions of time where s is the initial letter of second, m is the initial letter of minute, h is hour.......y is year

7. X; the letters used as Roman numerals

8. D for Decagon; where T stands for triangle, Q for Quadrilateral, P for Pentagon.......D for Decagon

9. 4; One has three letters, Two has three letters, Three has five letters...Nine has four letters

10. P for Pawn; chess pieces in order of decreasing importance

11. J; the sequence of consonants

12. 28; add 2 to the first number, then 3 to the second number, 4 to the fourth etc

13. X; letters with a horizontal axis of symmetry

14. 7; the digits arranged in alphabetical order

15. S for Spades; the suits of playing cards

16. N; these are the final letters of One, Two, Three....Ten

17. N; convert each number to its Roman numeral equivalent. It then reads FIVESIXSEVE, so the next letter is N

18. S for Sagittarius; the initial letters of the signs of the Zodiac

19. 1904; leap years

20. S for Seven; the initial letters of the names of the playing cards where A is for Ace, K for King, Q for Queen....S for Seven

21. R for Ruth; the initial letters of the books of the Old Testament

22. 1000; the binary numbers – or numbers consisting of ones and zeros only – in increasing order

23. K for Kansas; the American states in alphabetical order

24. E; the second letter in the name of each month

25. 293; numbers from 20 to 30 grouped in threes

6

PUZZLES & CONUNDRUMS

A chapter of devilishly difficult conundrums to drive you to distraction!

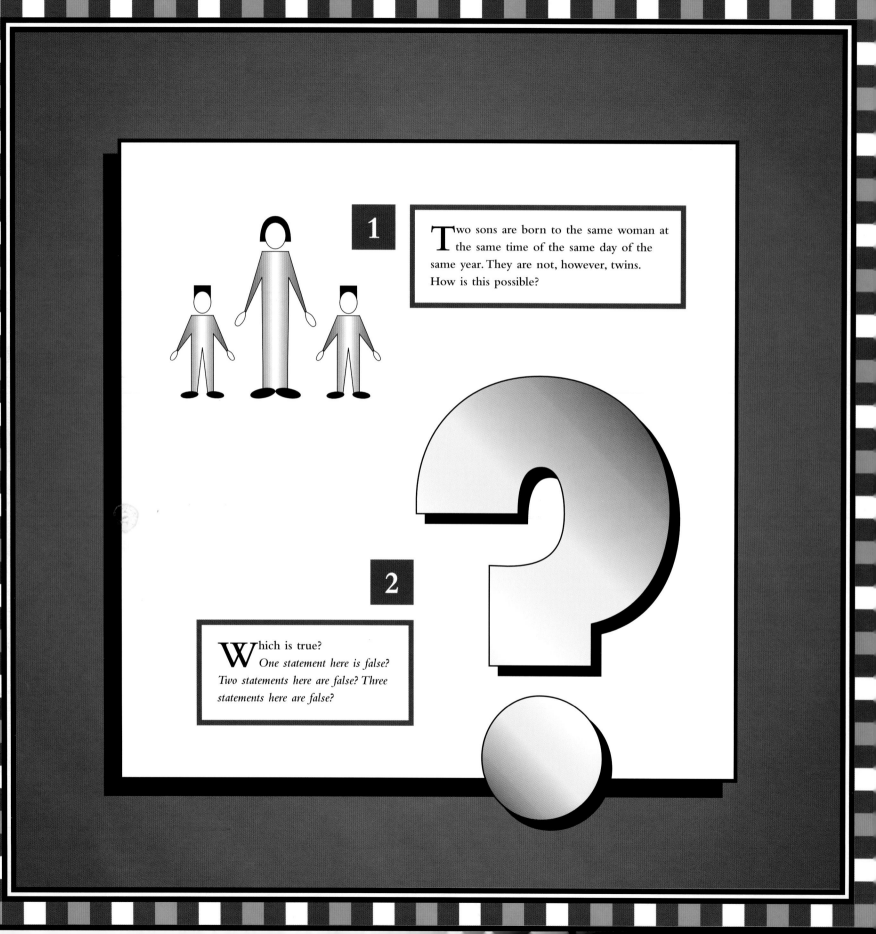

1 Two sons are born to the same woman at the same time of the same day of the same year. They are not, however, twins. How is this possible?

2 Which is true?
One statement here is false? Two statements here are false? Three statements here are false?

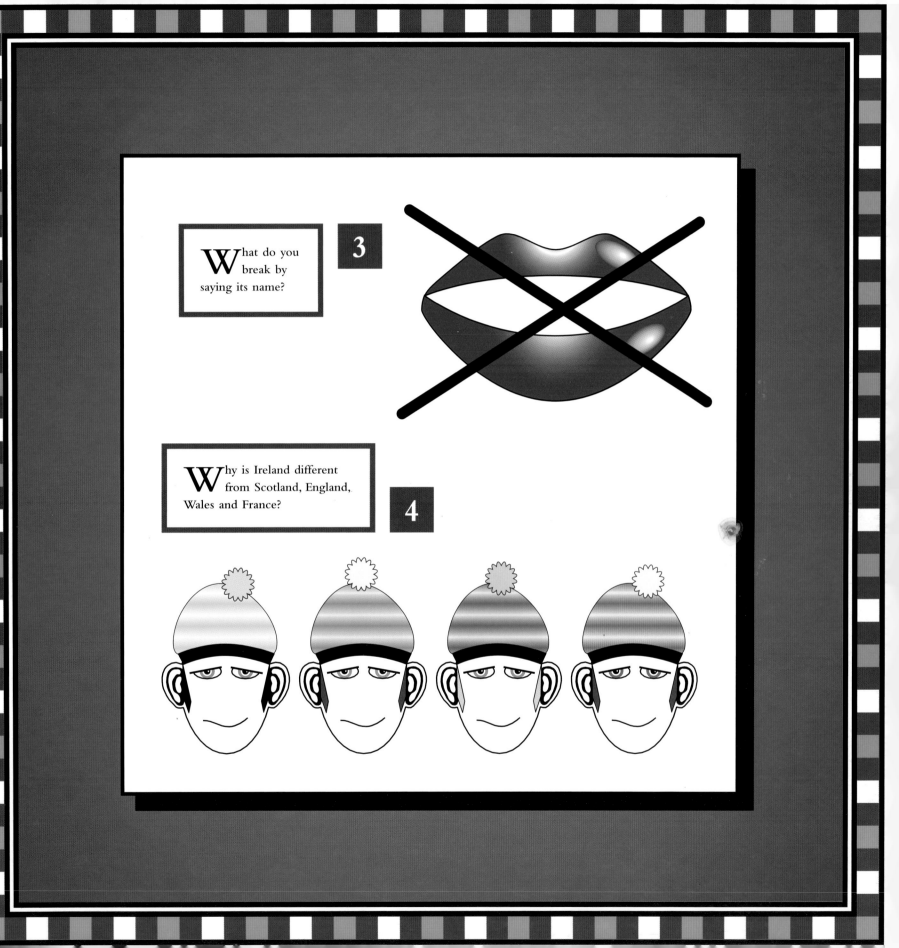

5

Complete this calculation without the aid of pen, paper, calculator or abacus!

Take a million
Divide it by four
Divide the result by five
Divide the result by two
Divide the new result by twenty
Subtract fifty
Divide by three
Divide that result by eight
Subtract one
Divide the result by seven
Add two
Divide the result by three
Add two
And divide the result by five

CALMNESS
CANOPY
DEFT
FIRST
SIGHING
STUN

6

These words share a common feature. What is it?

What are the next two symbols in this series?

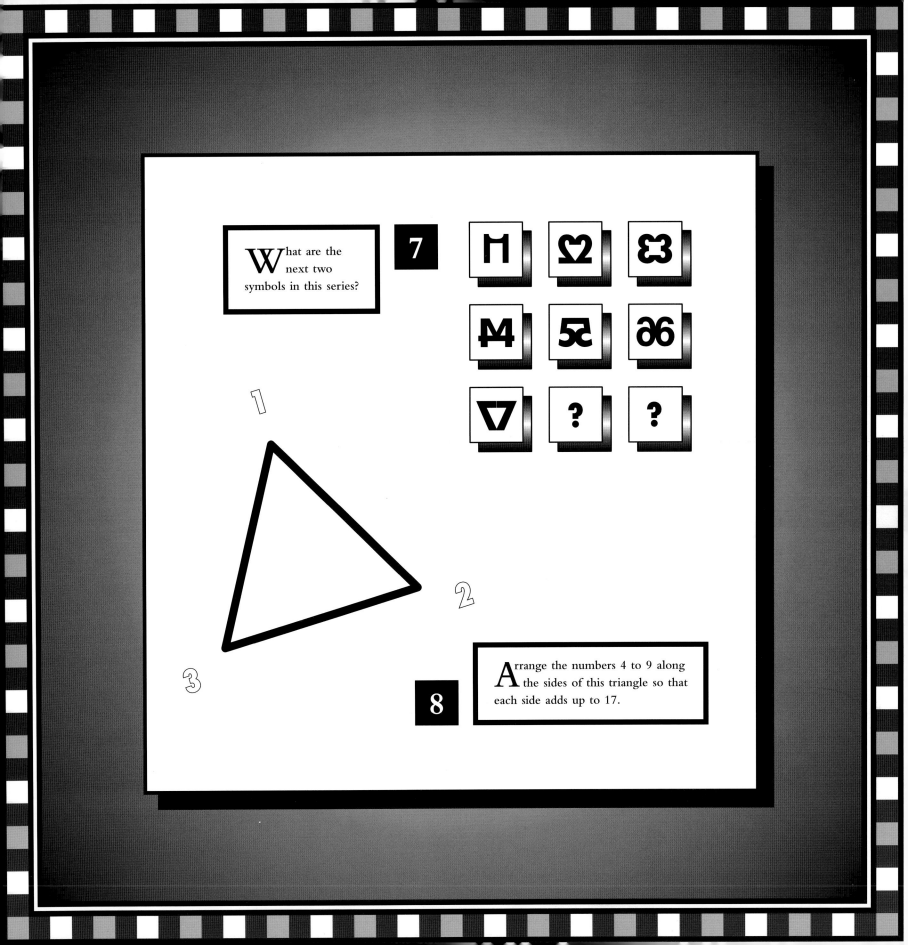

Arrange the numbers 4 to 9 along the sides of this triangle so that each side adds up to 17.

I've got ten or more daughters. I've got less than ten daughters. I've got at least one daughter. If only one of these statements is true, how many daughters have I got?

9

Which is the odd one out?

10

10?

EGG

FISH

TABLE

FOUNDATION

BET

A driver notches up 15951 miles on his milometer, and realises that this number is palindromic, reading the same backwards as forwards. He feels pleased to have noticed such a rare occurrence, and is thus doubly surprised when, two hours later, another palindromic number appears. How fast was he driving during those two hours?

11

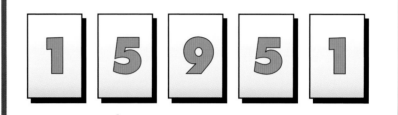

When asked who a certain photograph was of, the owner replied "I have neither sister nor brother, but my mother's daughter is that man's mother". Who was in the photograph?

12

A woman has three daughters who in turn, each have three daughters. If they all get together in one room:–

13

1. How many pairs of sisters are present?

2. How many pairs of mothers and daughters are there?

3. How many pairs of aunts and nieces are there?

4. How many pairs of cousins are there?

5. How many pairs of grandmothers and granddaughters are there?

6. How many people are there in the room?

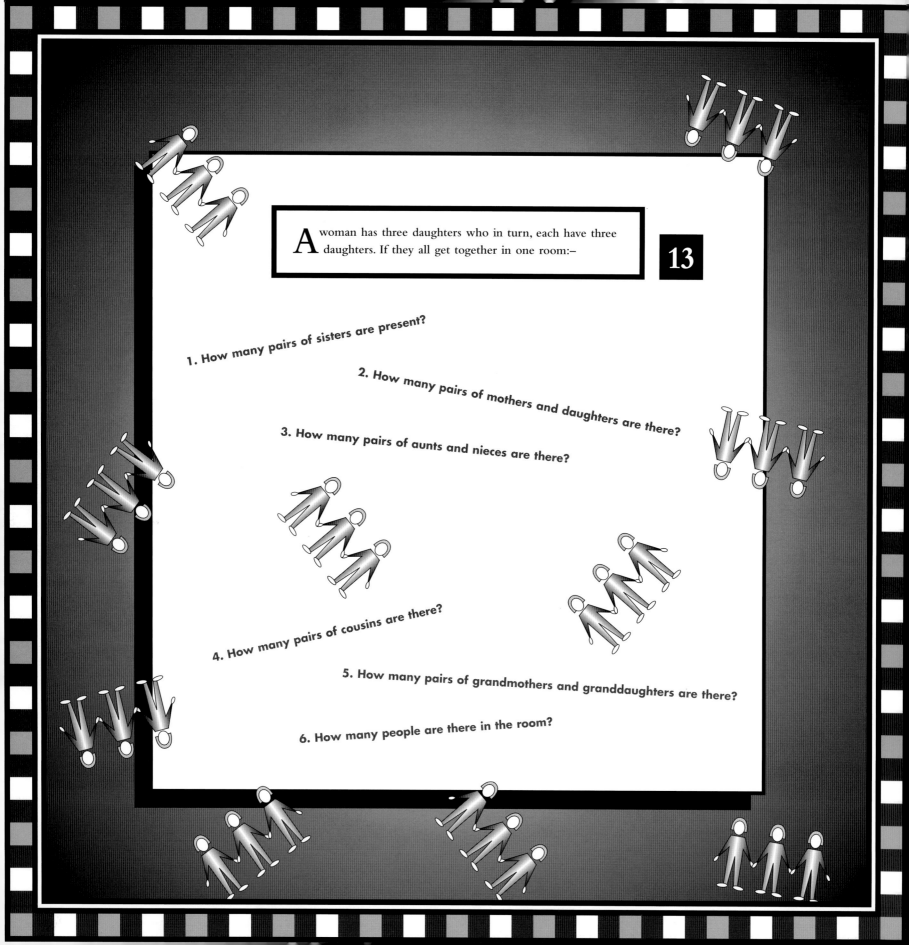

THIS SENTANCE CONTAINES TWO MISSTAKES.

How many mistakes are there in the sentence above?

14

My friend Sarah told me that her grandmother was younger than her mother. Could this be true?

15

1. Exactly one of these statements is false
2. **Exactly two of these statements are false**
3. Exactly three of these statements are false
4. **Exactly four of these statements are false**
5. Exactly five of these statements are false
6. **Exactly six of these statements are false**
7. Exactly seven of these statements are false
8. **Exactly eight of these statements are false**
9. Exactly nine of these statements are false
10. **Exactly ten of these statements are false**

How many of these statements are true?

16

PUZZLES & CONUNDRUMS - SOLUTIONS

1. They are triplets

2. Two statements here are false

3. Silence

4. It's got three vowels

5. The answer is one

6. Three letters in each word are in their normal alphabetical order eg LMN, NOP, DEF, RST, GHI and STU

7. The symbols are mirror image numbers, the sequence is 1, 2, 3, 4, 5, 6 and 7, so the next two are:

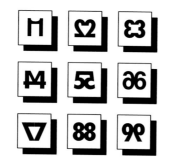

8.

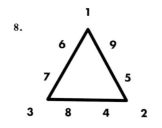

9. None. If "I've got at least one daughter" is true, then "I've got ten or more daughters" can also be true, and vice versa. "I've got less than ten daughters" can be true by itself, but only if I have no daughters.

10. You can't lay a fish

11. The next palindromic number after 15951 is 16061, so he must have travelled 110 miles, giving him an average speed of 55 miles per hour

12. It was the owner's son

13. 1) 12
    2) 12
    3) 18
    4) 27
    5) 9
    6) 13

14. Four - three spelling mistakes plus the mistaken claim that it only contains two mistakes

15. It is quite possible that her paternal grandmother could be younger than her mother. If her mother is 58 and her father 24, her father's mother could be 44.

16. All statements contradict each other, therefore one at most can be true - statement 9 - the others are all false.

BRAIN TEASERS

**You may think you are smart,
but are you ready for this challenge?**

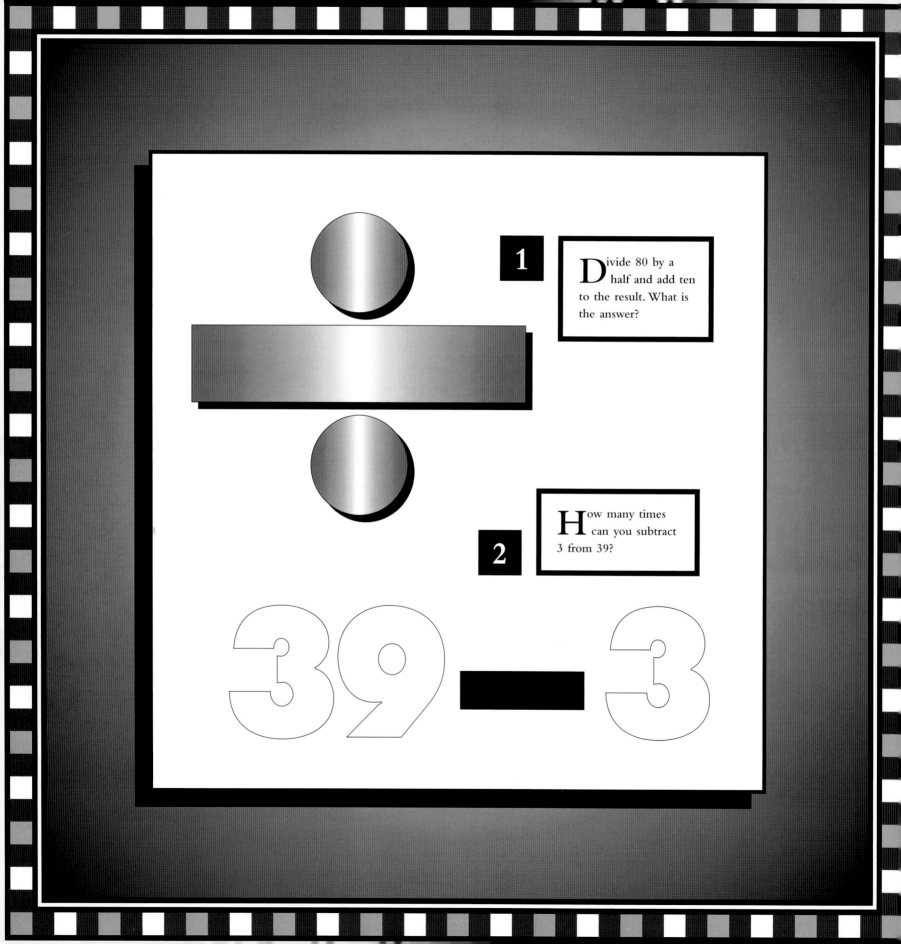

1 Divide 80 by a half and add ten to the result. What is the answer?

2 How many times can you subtract 3 from 39?

39 – 3

171

3 — Add 2 to 171 and make it less than eighteen.

4 — How many string quartets are there in a dozen?

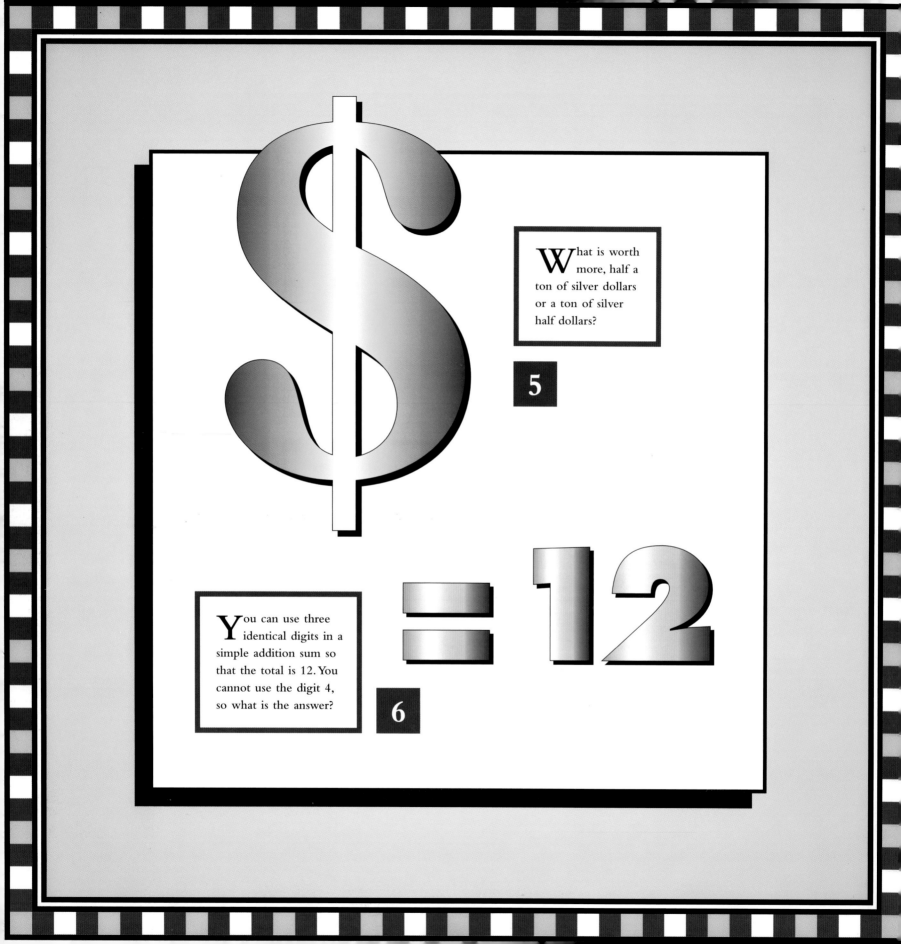

What is worth more, half a ton of silver dollars or a ton of silver half dollars?

5

You can use three identical digits in a simple addition sum so that the total is 12. You cannot use the digit 4, so what is the answer?

6

$ = 12

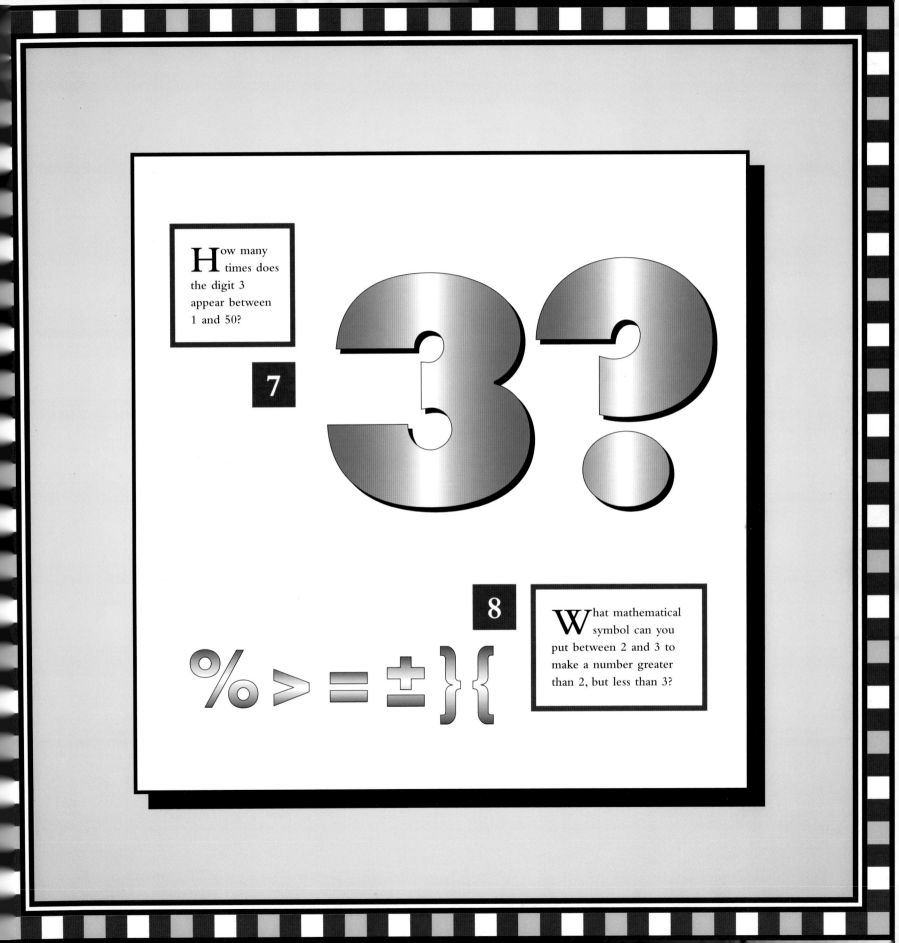

How many times does the digit 3 appear between 1 and 50?

7

What mathematical symbol can you put between 2 and 3 to make a number greater than 2, but less than 3?

8

BRAIN TEASERS - SOLUTIONS

1. 170

2. Once. After that you're subtracting 3 from 36, and so on

3. $17\frac{1}{2}$

4. 12

5. A ton of silver half dollars

6. $11 + 1 = 12$

7. 15 times: 3, 13, 23, 30, 31, 32, 33 (two 3s!), 34, 35, 36, 37, 38, 39, 43

8. A decimal point

8

LETTER PUZZLES

We all know there are 3 sides to a triangle, 4 seasons in a year and 5 rings in the Olympic standard but can you work out 6 = F in a F?

Answer: 6 Feet in a Fathom

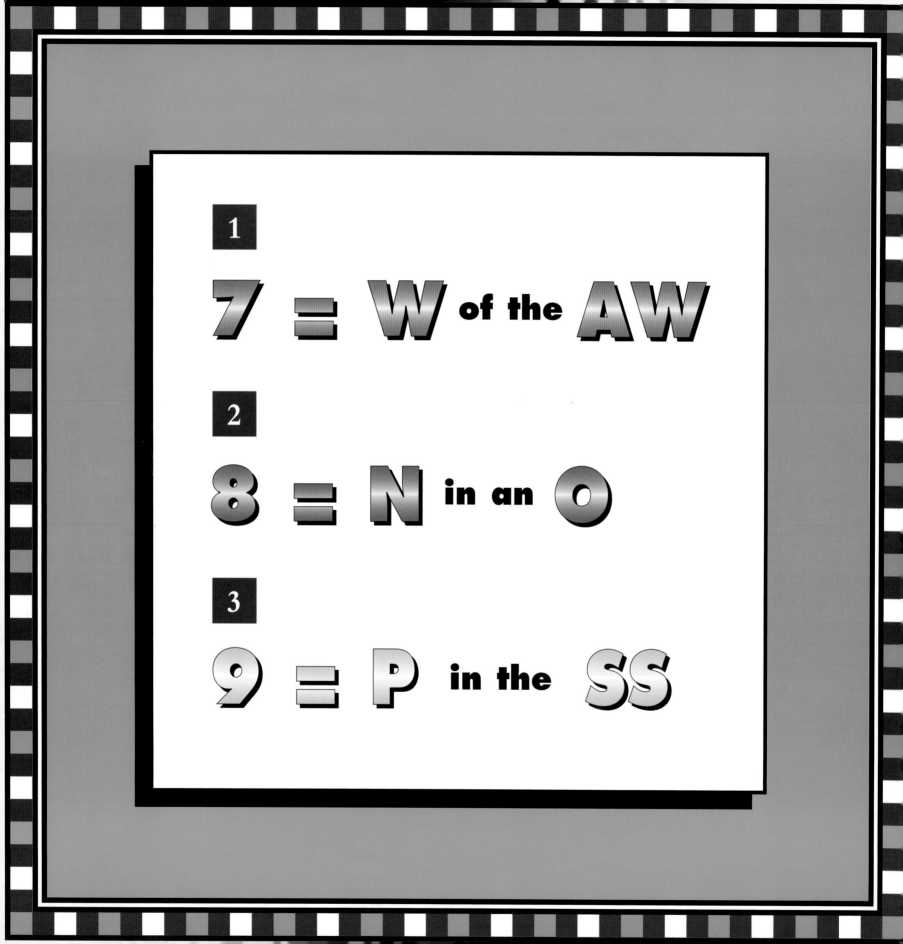

1

7 = W of the AW

2

8 = N in an O

3

9 = P in the SS

4

12 = D of C

5

13 = C in a S

6

14 = L in a S

7

18 = H on a GC

8

21 = S on a D

9

22 = L of the HA

10

26 = M in a M

11

27 = B in the NT

12

54 = C in a P

13

55 = B on a R

14

64 = S on a CB

15

88 = K on a P

16

114 = C in the K

17

213 = B in the HB

18

1440 = M in a D

LETTER PUZZLES – SOLUTIONS

1. 7 Wonders of the Ancient World

2. 8 Notes in an Octave

3. 9 Planets in the Solar System

4. 12 Days of Christmas

5. 13 Cards in a Suit

6. 14 Lines in a Sonnet

7. 18 Holes on a Golf Course

8. 21 Spots on a Dice

9. 22 Letters of the Hebrew Alphabet

10. 26 Miles in a Marathon

11. 27 Books in the New Testament

12. 54 Cards in a Pack

13. 55 Beads on a Rosary

14. 64 Squares on a Chess Board

15. 88 Keys on a Piano

16. 114 Chapters in the Koran

17. 213 Bones in the Human Body

18. 1440 Minutes in a Day